Opportunities in the

BIOLOGICAL SCIENCES

by Charles A. Winter, Ph.D.

Vocational Guidance Manuals

EDUCATIONAL BOOKS DIVISION OF
UNIVERSAL PUBLISHING AND DISTRIBUTING CORPORATION
NEW YORK

VOCATIONAL GUIDANCE MANUALS
Published by Universal Publishing and
Distributing Corporation
235 East 45 Street
New York, N.Y. 10017

Manufactured in the
United States of America

ABOUT THE AUTHOR

DR. CHARLES A. Winter is a former full-time research worker in pharmacology at the Merck Institute for Therapeutic Research. In 1967, at the time of his retirement, he accepted appointment as Professor of Pharmacology at Woman's Medical College in Philadelphia. He also retained a consultantship with his former employer, Merck Institute.

The author's entire adult life has been devoted to bioscience. After receiving the A.B. degree with a major in biology from Southwestern College, Winfield, Kansas in 1926, he studied zoology at the University of California and at The Johns Hopkins University. He then accepted an appointment as Instructor in Biology at the University of Buffalo. While teaching at Buffalo, he took graduate work in physiology and received his Ph.D. in 1935. He then taught physiology at Buffalo, and subsequently at the University of Iowa and the University of Oklahoma, rising to the rank of Associate Professor.

Dr. Winter is the author of nearly a hundred technical papers in scientific journals, review articles, and sections of monographs. He has been an invited lecturer at many international meetings both in the U.S.A. and abroad. He was elected a Fellow in the American Association for the Advancement of Science and the New York Academy of Sciences, and became a member by invitation of the Royal Society of Medicine in London, and of the Swiss Society of Physiology, Physiological Chemistry, and Pharmacology. He is also a former chairman of the Gordon Research Conference on Medicinal Chemistry, sponsored by the American Association for the Advancement of Science.

He is a member of the American Physiological Society, the Society for Experimental Biology and Medicine, the American Society for Pharmacology and Experimental Therapeutics, the American Institute of Biological Sciences, and other scientific organizations.

ACKNOWLEDGMENTS

BIOLOGICAL SCIENCE IS too vast and complex to be fully understood by any one person, and it is changing too rapidly for any publication to be wholly accurate and up-to-date. Your author will agree in advance with any critic that this book must have errors both of omission and of commission, but I hope not so many as to prevent the book from being useful. Your suggestions for improvement (in case there should be opportunity for future alterations) will be gratefully received.

Several people were of great help in the preparation of this work.

Dr. Elwood B. Ehrle, Office of Biological Education, American Institute of Biological Sciences, made many valuable suggestions for and criticisms of the opening chapters.

Dr. Richard S. Cowan, Director of the Museum of Natural History, U.S. National Museum, made important contributions of background material which were invaluable in the discussion of systematic biology.

Dr. Howell V. Daly, Division of Entomology, University of California, and a former chairman of the Educational Committee of the Society of Systematic Zoology, read several portions of the manuscript and was especially helpful in the section on biosystematics.

Much of the factual content of the book could not have
been included without the helpful cooperation of several colleagues in bioscience who supplied background material. Among
others, I wish to acknowledge:

Dr. Howard C. Hopps, Armed Forces Institute of
Pathology

Dr. C. A. Price, Professor of Plant Biochemistry, Rut-
gers University

Dr. William J. Zaumeyer, Principal Pathologist, Vegetables and Ornamentals Research Branch, Agricultural Research Service, Crops Research Division, U. S.
Department of Agriculture

Finally, I must express appreciation to certain members of
my family. My son-in-law, Mr. Norman J. Smith, read several
portions of the manuscript from the point of view of a junior
high school science teacher and made several helpful suggestions. My elder son, Dr. Donald F. Winter, also read several
sections of the manuscript from the viewpoint of a physical
scientist.

But most important of all, the whole project would have
been impossible without the enthusiastic cooperation of my
wife, who is the only person who had the patience and persis-
tence to read every word at all stages of development of the
manuscript. Some 40 years ago, one biologist, whose name I no
longer recall, dedicated a work to his wife because, although she
was wholly nonscientific, she had devoted her entire life to the
advancement of science. I echo those sentiments.

Although all of the above—and others—contributed to
whatever merits the book has, I alone am responsible for the
contents, and none of the others can share the blame for its
deficiencies.

                          Charles A. Winter, Ph.D.
                          Blue Bell, Pennsylvania
                          February, 1970

CONTENTS

vii

CHAPTER 1

A PANORAMIC VIEW OF BIOLOGY

ACCORDING TO A SURVEY published in *Science* several years ago, high school students sometimes have bizarre and unflattering notions about what scientists are like. A third of them thought that scientists cannot have normal family lives and are unlikely to marry and have children. One out of five thought that scientists have little regard for humanity or concern for the general welfare, and many expressed a feeling that there is something "evil" about science.

Such views suggest familiarity with fictional presentations, such as the Frankenstein movies or the Dr. Jekyll-Mr. Hyde type of stories but not with real scientists. Scientists are enthusiastic about their work, and they spend most of their waking hours thinking and talking about it, but usually they are not so preoccupied as to be prevented from indulging in the same pastimes as do other educated and cultured people. According to one survey, 90% are married; they have an average of two children each. Cultural interests among scientists are as varied as among other people, and range all the way from enthusiasm for sports to participation in amateur theatrical performances.

9

We sometimes hear about a "gap" between scientists on the one hand and the devotees of the humanities on the other hand. But actually, most scientists are deeply interested in one or more aspects of the humanities, and some writers have expressed the view that the real gap is between those who continue to use their brains after finishing school—whether they are scientists or nonscientists—and those who do not. Any one who does not wish to use his intellect in his daily pursuits would be equally out of place in a scientific career or in any other academic discipline.

Biologists are the targets of some special sorts of misconceptions. To some, the word *biologist* may conjure up an image of a rather shabbily-dressed, absent-minded, middle-aged professor forever roaming about fields and meadows with a butterfly net in his hand or interminably peering through bird glasses. Now, it is perfectly true that collecting insects or observing wildlife—birds or other creatures—is a legitimate occupation of certain kinds of biologists. One who studies insects is an *entomologist* and the specialist in birds is an *ornithologist*, but as we shall see in a later chapter, there is a lot more to being an entomologist or an ornithologist than just watching or collecting these captivating creatures. Such observation and collection are not the exclusive domain of the professional biologist. Many amateurs have found these activities to be a fascinating hobby.

Some biologists are experimental scientists and the experimental biologist must of necessity make observations on living organisms. These organisms vary in complexity all the way from bacteria to man himself. The elucidation of the functions of the human body has been made possible only by observations made upon the bodies of animals most nearly resembling man; that is, the mammals. Many people misunderstand animal experimentation, and you no doubt have heard the accusations of those who depict the experimental biologist as cruel and sadistic, inflicting unnecessary pain and suffering upon his victims. These people have had no experience in experimental biology laboratories. After 40 years of experience in such laboratories and acquaintance with many hundreds of workers in them, I can only say that the cruel and sadistic experimenter must be a rare bird indeed—I have never met one. There have been cases, however, in which workers unable to learn careful and sympathetic handling of animals were dismissed from their jobs. Some experimenters have also voiced criticism of others who in their opinion were not sufficiently careful to avoid suffering or pain. Most experimenters know what their detractors fail to appreciate; namely, that observations made under conditions of extreme stress on the part of the animal subject cannot be considered to be made under "normal" conditions and in most instances the results might be invalid as answers to the question under investigation.

If you are considering a career in biology, and if experimental biology appeals to you, you need have no fear that you will be in the company of unfeeling and inhuman monsters. By and large, people with inferior mental capacity rarely succeed in obtaining advanced degrees in any academic discipline. This is surely as true in the biological sciences as in other subjects. And although an occasional person of high intelligence may have a warped attitude toward his fellow creatures, even a casual observer must have noted that the so-called "intellectual community" leads in urging mankind toward a deepening of understanding of all life and a lessening of cruelty, including an abhorrence of that most cruel of all activities, warfare. Moreover of all people, the biologist must have a deep appreciation for all forms of life and a reverence for life itself.

THE VARIETIES OF BIOLOGICAL SCIENCES

ALTHOUGH WE OFTEN speak of biology as a science, it

is really a group of sciences, variously referred to as "biological sciences," "biosciences," or "life sciences." All are concerned one way or another with life or with living creatures, but biologists vary widely in the work they do. The *American Institute of Biological Sciences* (AIBS for short) has called biology "the most intriguing and pervasive of sciences" and has characterized it as "actually a multiscience composed of many disciplines unified by the fact that all living things—plants, animals, and microorganisms—follow the same fundamental laws of heredity, reproduction, growth, development, self-maintenance, and response." Biology not only deals with living matter, but is itself a lively and "jumping" subject, with almost unlimited opportunities for the active participants in tomorrow's world.

In later chapters, we shall describe in some detail many of the biosciences, but it will not be out of place to give some idea at this point how wide a range of careers is available to those trained in biology. The classification of biologists as either botanists, zoologists, or microbiologists gives little hint of the wide variety of biological disciplines that exist. One kind of zoologist, for example, is the *taxonomist* or *systematist,* specializing in the identification, description, and classification of animals and determining how a given species fits into the scheme of nature.

Seldom will the interests of a zoological systematist range over the whole animal kingdom; he is more likely to specialize to some extent. If, for example, he mainly studies mammals, he is a *mammologist,* if reptiles, a *herpetologist,* if fish, an *ichthyologist,* if protozoa, a *protozoologist,* and so on. Botanists and microbiologists can be systematists, too, or the interests of some systematists may range across the boundaries between plants and animals—there are some "generalists."

Bioscientists of several categories are fascinated by the structural details of organisms—they are *anatomists* or *morphologists.* If the microscopic structure of tissues is the object of the morphologist's scrutiny, he is a *histologist*. Still more detailed study of the structure within each individual cell makes him a *cytologist*. If all this sounds like morphology is a lifeless and dull subject, the impression is far from the truth. The cytologist, for example, is keenly aware of the relationship between the structural components of a cell and cellular functions. So, cell morphology becomes a background for other branches of *cellular biology,* such as *cellular physiology* and *biochemistry*. The *molecular biologist* is preoccupied with an even more intimate examination of the ultimate mechanisms within a cell.

From this brief survey, you can see that the interests of bioscientists range all the way from a systematic examination of whole groups of plants or animals (or both) down to the level of the molecules that make up cells. But that is only the beginning! No group of plants or animals exists by itself. All groups and individuals interact with each other and each has a niche which it fills in the scheme of nature. Its whole surroundings form an "ecosystem," so another biological science, *ecology,* is born.

The laws governing heredity occupy the attention of the bioscience of *genetics*. Geneticists may apply mathematics, anatomy, biochemistry, or a host of other disciplines in their efforts. The lines between different biological vocations are often rather poorly defined and there is much overlap. For example, if a life scientist is interested in the genetics of bacteria, is he a geneticist or a bacteriologist? If his favorite subject is the embryonic development within the egg of a reptile, is he an *embryologist* or a *herpetologist?* The botanist who writes papers on diseases of trees caused by fungi—is he a *mycologist* (student of fungi), a *dendrologist* (expert on trees), or a *plant pathologist* (concerned with diseases of plants)? In each case, he is a bit of each, and can classify himself according to what his primary interests are—and this may change during different stages of his career.

Wildlife biologists are concerned with animals, fish, or fowl of the wild, and *marine biologists* are fascinated by the richness of life in the sea, but either may concentrate on taxonomy, physiology, ecology, or any of several other specialties.

Several biological disciplines are not only basic sciences but also have important applications. Examples of these would be those plant and animal sciences which may be applied to agriculture or forestry. Some also have important applications in health and disease of man or other animals. Collectively, the latter are sometimes referred to as "biomedical sciences." Included in this group are certain aspects of anatomy, physiology, biochemistry, and microbiology—which we have already mentioned—together with *biophysics, nutrition, pharmacology,* and *pathology.* When the public press mentions "the advances of medical science" the reference is usually to reports of research in one or more of these biosciences. There are, of course, many other life sciences with practical applications; indeed, any biological specialty you can think of has both its basic science and its practical aspects.

The career activities of a bioscientist may involve teaching, research, administration, service work, or industrial production. If you choose to become a biologist, you may specialize in one of these activities, or a combination of two or more, or you may switch from one to another at various stages of your career. If you teach, it may be in secondary school, college or university, or in a professional school, such as medicine, dentistry, pharmacy, forestry, or agriculture. If you do research, you may spend your time in experimentation, or your research may involve the observation of natural events—in either case you will classify, analyze, and interpret your observations.

In succeeding chapters, you will find that career opportunities for biologists are almost everywhere—in educational institutions, governmental installations (federal, state, and local), private research foundations, zoos, botanical gardens, aquariums, arboretums, natural history museums, and in an astonishingly wide variety of industrial and business concerns.

ORGANIZATIONS IN THE FIELD

HUMAN NATURE IMPELS people to form associations of those having mutual interests and enthusiasms. Biologists are no exception, and there is a bewildering variety of organizations of professional biologists. These societies serve both a social function and as a means of communication. By far the largest organization of biologists is the American Institute of Biological Sciences, whose goal is to enroll all professional biologists as members. Each specialty in bioscience boasts its own society— such organizations as American Association of Anatomists, American Society of Cell Biology, Botanical Society of America, and so on. AIBS includes 45 of these associations as "adherent members," 10 regional organizations as "affiliate members," and 18 companies as "industrial members." Together, these represent more than 80,000 biologists. In addition, 14,000 biologists are individual members, and there are a growing number of student chapters in campuses across the country.

The AIBS provides many activities in order to merit the support of biologists. It collaborates with the National Science Foundation in keeping up-to-date records of biographical and professional information concerning bioscientists. It operates a placement service for life scientists seeking employment. It makes life insurance available for members at group rates. Official publications, such as the semi-monthly, *BioScience,* keep members informed on current interests of biology and biological education. AIBS has advisory committees for various governmental ogencies, and seeks to improve the links between physical anl life sciences by its operation of the *BioInstrumentation Advisory Council* (BIAC).

The Office of Biological Education (OBE) of AIBS is of special importance to students or to anyone contemplating a bioscience career. OBE is actively engaged in career guidance, and handles some 125 letters each week from students, faculty, guidance counselors, and others. It has prepared a brochure on *Careers in Biology* and helps in the distribution of career brochures of several adherent societies (See Appendix). OBE operates a consultant bureau which sends out informational packets, and sponsors visits of biologists to high schools and colleges. OBE has been responsible for the *AIBS Directory of BioScience Departments in the United States and Canada.* It also sponsors small conferences and refresher courses. The Office has shown special interest in recruitment and training of biological technicians, and in the biological programs offered by two-year colleges. In many of these activities OBE works closely with other agencies of AIBS, notably the BIAC and the Commission on Undergraduate Education in the Biological Sciences (CUEBS).

The AIBS conducts several kinds of meetings of biologists, especially the regular annual meeting, which gives those in attendance a chance to discuss problems of mutual interest, to present papers on their latest research, and so on. Many biologists also attend the annual meeting of the American Association for the Advancement of Science, that great interdisciplinary body which embraces all of science—physical, biological, and social. Many specialized biological societies, national and local, also hold meetings. But the world's largest scientific meeting is the annual convention of the Federation of Societies for Experimental Biology held each spring around Easter time. In a recent typical year, 22,000 registrants listened to more than 3,500 short papers in which speakers outlined results and conclusions of their latest experiments and observations. In addition, there were 133 longer lectures by specially invited speakers in 26 organized symposia—each symposium was made up of a group of lectures organized around a central theme. It made for a busy week.

All of this may sound rather awesome to the beginner, but it deserves to be mentioned that a high proportion of the papers was presented by the youngest group in attendance—the graduate students, and nearly three-quarters of the registrants had not yet achieved membership in any of the societies of the Federation. The Federation consists of six societies of experimental biologists (see Appendix) in some of the areas of biomedical science—physiology, biochemistry, pharmacology, pathology, nutrition, and immunology. Unlike the AIBS, the Federation does not accept individual members, and the individual societies generally restrict their memberships only to those who have demonstrated aptitude in biological experimentation. Nonmembers, especially students, are encouraged to attend meetings and present papers. Very few societies outside the Federation have such restricted membership policies; in general, it is sufficient for an individual to express an interest in the aims of the society in order to qualify for membership.

THE DEMAND FOR BIOLOGISTS

IT IS DIFFICULT to appreciate the rate at which science has grown and continues to grow. It is frequently said that more than 90% of the scientists who have ever lived are alive and working today. Biology has shared with other sciences in this startling growth. According to an estimate by the U. S. Department of Labor, the single decade of the 1960's has seen the demand for biological and agricultural scientists increase by about 75%. The number of Ph.D.'s awarded in the biosciences in the United States in the 1960's was *ten times* as great as in the 1920's.

The rapid growth of colleges and universities, including the establishment of many new community colleges, is increasing the demand for teachers of biology. Industry, too, absorbs more and more biologists. To take an example of one industry: expenditures for research and development in the pharmaceutical industry have a little more than doubled each five years during the past two decades. In terms of dollars, this has meant an increase from about $39 million in 1950 to $750 million by 1970. Salaries for research personnel account for the major share of this expenditure, and most of the research workers are either biologists or chemists.

Examples of the demand for biologists are given in official statements of biological societies. The American Physiological Society, for example, says "there are more positions available to physiologists than persons to fill them." According to the American Phytopathological Society, "there is need for many more (plant pathologists) than the number presently being trained." The American Society for Pharmacology and Experimental Therapeutics states "there is now an acute shortage of pharmacologists in the United States . . . new laboratories for pharmacology are being created . . . much faster than they can be filled with competent pharmacologists. Today, many research projects in pharmacology cannot be tackled because of the lack of trained manpower." The American Society of Biological Chemists goes on record: "For some time to come, biochemistry will be one of the most rapidly growing fields of science . . . the demand for biochemists is great and the opportunities are numerous." And here is the Ecological Society of America: "there is an ever-growing demand for well-trained ecologists."

The government has an urgent need for biologically trained men and women. The U. S. Department of Agriculture alone employs more than 20,000 biologists. The National Academy of Sciences has estimated that there are 50,000 to 75,000 agricultural scientists—or nearly one-fifth of all scientists—whose work and education directly involve biology. According to an estimate by the National Science Foundation, colleges during the 1960's needed to increase the number of biologists employed as professors and instructors by some 50%. This is equivalent to a demand for nearly 20,000 new biologists.

There is little doubt, then, that the future is bright with opportunities for those embarking upon a biological career. A satisfying and full life awaits the man or woman who has the personal attributes needed to be a good scientist and who is willing and able to achieve the educational level required.

THE BIOLOGY TEACHER

SOME TIME DURING a biologist's career, he (or she) will make a choice whether to devote his time to teaching, research, or some other activity. In many instances, the beginning student can postpone the choice, but it should not be out of place for him to think about it at an early stage of his career. The preparation for teaching in high school or junior college includes, in addition to courses in biology and other sciences, certain courses in teaching methods and in science education. Many teachers in four year colleges and universities could, perhaps, benefit from some exposure to "teaching methods," but it is not required of them. Likewise, the many kinds of service work performed in practical applications of biology do not require "education" courses.

The largest market for teaching skills in biology is the classroom of the secondary school. The National Education Association estimated that in 1966 nearly 3,000 new biology teachers were required to replace teachers retiring or leaving, and to fill vacancies created by school expansions. When one considers that the enrollment in high school biology classes projected for 1975 is *two million more* than in 1955, it is easy to see that employment opportunities for biology teachers will continue to be high.

The biology teacher in secondary school is a professional teacher who has specialized in biology. Although he (or she) will seldom be an active research worker, he will continue his education by study, summer school, meetings and conferences, and by reading articles in scientific journals. Biology is changing rapidly, and the biology of 1970 is not the same as it was in 1965 or as it will be in 1975. The demand to keep up to date is not less challenging for the biology teacher than for the research worker. A part of the job of teaching students to learn is to understand and apply the art of learning. The National Science Foundation supports summer institutes for college teachers, some of them especially for biology teachers, while the Office of Biological Education of the AIBS sponsors refresher courses as well as sessions on biological education relating to any and all levels of education from elementary school to university. Of special interest for the teacher in secondary school are the regional seminars sponsored by the National Association of Biology Teachers.

Some biology teachers have entered the profession from other disciplines simply because they find biology more interesting than their former employment. These recruits are sometimes teachers from other subjects and sometimes biologists who have worked in industrial or government laboratories or elsewhere. Most biology teachers, though, are specially trained. The college training for biology teachers in secondary schools should include a broad study of many biological subjects, including both laboratory and field work, and both plant and animal material. Courses in chemistry and physics are also essential; indeed, in some of the smaller schools, the biology teacher may be called upon to teach other sciences. The college student intending to teach biology should gain as much experience as possible in practice teaching under the supervision of experienced teachers. He will also find it advantageous to find summer employment in a biologically oriented job, such as work in medical or research laboratories, conservation projects, forests, etc.

Most biology teachers in elementary or secondary school have entered the profession immediately after completing college and obtaining a baccalaureate degree. If so, it is desirable to continue formal education through the Master's degree in spare time, evenings, summers, etc. The standards for high school teachers are being elevated, and in some of the better school systems the Master's diploma is the "ticket" for entrance. Training programs covering a five-year period and culminating in the Master's degree are available in many training centers for teachers. The Ph.D. or Sc.D. degree is primarily a research degree. In colleges and universities the doctorate diploma is often referred to as "the union card," and there are few successful careers in college or university teaching available for those without a doctorate. The secondary school teacher who has earned a Ph.D. degree, on the other hand, is the exception. This is just as well, for the emphasis on research which is necessary during the study for the doctorate is of limited value for the kind of work the high school teacher will be doing.

The high school teacher is a highly respected member of his community, and in recent years his prestige has grown. There are many rewards, both tangible and intangible, for the devoted teacher, working conditions and pay scales are constantly improving, and employment opportunities will exceed the supply of competent teachers for years to come.

Teaching in junior colleges and other institutions of higher learning will be discussed in some detail in Chapter 7, but at this point we should mention a controversy that has arisen regarding research activities of college teachers. Teachers in most colleges, universities, and professional schools spend part of their time teaching and part of it in research. This blend of teaching and research has given rise to many arguments. Both in professional journals and in the public press one often sees references to a supposed incompatibility between teaching and research. The excellent researcher is depicted as a poor teacher, and the teacher is accused of being incapable of doing good research. There are undoubtedly some good research workers who are incompetent teachers, and some good teachers who have little success in research, but some individuals seem to combine both skills to a high degree.

In its most extreme form, the idea that teaching and research are incompatible led to a recent suggestion that a university should create two faculties, one for teaching and one for research. Some would consider such a move to be contrary to the great tradition of the university that the pursuit of new knowledge is a prime source of the enthusiasm for his subject which every inspiring teacher must have. Most of the publications on the question are really expressions of opinion rather than facts, but a survey recently conducted in one large university showed that the teachers who were rated by the students as being the best instructors were also those most active in research. The survey, however, was conducted in a university highly oriented toward research, so possibly the question hasn't been finally settled.* In many universities, the rewards to faculty members in the form of promotions and salary increases are based upon research productivity (not necessarily the same as research excellence) as evidenced by authorship of papers or books, rather than upon teaching excellence—a situation which has given rise to the dictum "publish or perish."

This state of affairs does not mean that college administrators are not interested in good teaching, but it seems to exist because it is easier to judge productivity in research (though not necessarily quality) than creativity in teaching. As a result, research into the teaching of biology has lagged behind many

---

* Those interested in pursuing this point further may obtain the report *Teaching and Research,* Publication No. 23, CUEBS, 3900 Wisconsin Ave. N.W., Washington, D.C. 20016.

other kinds of research. Attempts at remedying this situation are being made by such groups as the Office of Biological Education of the AIBS, the Commission on Undergraduate Education in Biology (CUEBS), and the National Association of Biology Teachers (NABT). The NABT devoted one entire issue of their official journal, *The American Biology Teacher* (see Appendix) to "Careers in Biology Education"—including those inside and outside the classroom.

WOMEN IN BIOLOGY

ACCORDING TO THE 1960 census, more than half of all women scientists were either biologists or mathematicians. Those two sciences were about equally represented. Nevertheless, women are greatly under-represented in all sciences; only 9% of American scientists are women. Nobody today believes that this is a result of inferior ability on the part of women, and within recent years there is a trend toward increasing enrollment of women as undergraduates and as candidates for advanced degrees in science. Several studies on the use of human resources have pointed out that the relatively small numbers of women in scientific positions is not so much a result of the attitude of employers as it is a lack of applications from qualified women. There are opportunities in the biosciences for women, and too few women apply for them.

Bryn Mawr opened as a woman's college in 1875. It is said that at that time there were only four women Ph.D.'s in the world. Since Bryn Mawr hired only Ph.D.'s for its faculty, the faculty had to be made up of men. This situation has been changing at an accelerating pace. By 1920, 25 Ph.D. degrees were awarded to women in biological sciences. By 1940 the number was 86, and in 1960 150 women received Ph.D. degrees in one or another of the life sciences. The number is still rising, but should rise faster.

The reasons for the reluctance of women to undertake a scientific career are complex. Formerly, some held that a woman entering this field was intruding upon a man's world. Few would accept such a view today. The requirements for a woman in biology are exactly the same as for a man: a serious interest in the subject, a willingness to spend the time and effort necessary to train for it, and a desire to contribute to its advancement. This does not mean that the woman takes on masculine traits. She can remain feminine and still do a good job. As Ethaline Cortelyou put it: "Be a woman and be glad of it. Lipsticks and slipsticks are entirely compatible, and a pretty hat does not mean the head under it is empty." Alice Rossi (see Appendix) expressed the view that the bias which many girls have against a scientific career has its origin in the earliest family influences. Whether that is so or not, a report by the U. S. Department of Labor pointed out that women have amply demonstrated their scientific abilities by achievements in every field of science.

Some woman scientists work at a slower pace or even stop entirely for a time while raising a family. Since science advances rapidly, they have to work hard to catch up later in life. Nevertheless, many women do manage it, and remain successful scientists. For example, a girl and two boys have not prevented Dr. Evelyn Shaw, of the American Museum of Natural History, from carrying on research in the Caribbean, Mediterranean, and Aegean Seas, and becoming internationally known for her work on animal behavior as illustrated by the schooling of fishes.*

Not all women in bioscience complete the requirements for advanced degrees, and many women find satisfaction in working as laboratory assistants, technicians, and medical technolo-

---

* For an account of her work, see "The Schooling of Fishes," by Evelyn Shaw, *Scientific American,* June, 1962.

gists, and in related jobs. Indeed, the majority of such workers are women, as are large numbers of biology teachers at all levels of education from elementary school to university. An individual with a very high degree of competence may occasionally rise to a position of great responsibility and become eminent in her profession, even without the usual advanced degrees. The late Rachel Carson, for example, did not obtain a Doctor's degree, but she made a great impression by her biological writings—the best known was *Silent Spring*—and in her job she rose to the position of Editor-in-Chief of publications for the U. S. Wildlife Service.

According to a report by the U. S. Department of Labor, an educated woman is likely to seek employment outside the home, not merely for financial reward, but even more for those intangible rewards that come from solid achievement, recognition by one's fellow man, and service to society.

NEGROES IN BIOLOGY

MOST MINORITY GROUPS have fared well in science, including biology, but the black man is definitely underrepresented in proportion to his numbers in society. It would be easy to place the blame for this situation entirely on racial prejudice and antiblack discrimination. Prejudicial practices do exist, of course, but discriminaton has not prevented a few Negroes from achieving distinction in biology. In my own specialty—pharmacology—for example, I have several black colleagues who are not only well known for their research, but are active in the affairs of their professional society, and who have risen to the very top ranks of the academic world by becoming full professors or associate professors (the two highest titles in the hierarchy of the faculty) in universities of the highest caliber. A few Negroes have also achieved prominence in bioscience in privately supported laboratories, or in the laboratories of government or industry.

Among the latter is Dr. John T. Wilson, who is head of the Biological Science Research Laboratories of Lockheed Missiles & Space Co., where he has charge of many laboratories, including those of biochemistry, histopathology, microbiology, physiology, and toxicology. Most laboratories supported by industry advertise themselves as equal opportunity employers; frankly, I do not know whether all of them conscientiously live up to this slogan, but some of them, at least, really do. An interview with Dr. Wilson was published in the magazine *Scientific Research* (see Appendix). He thought that an important reason why black people don't go into science in greater numbers is that science is not usually presented to the young black student as something he can and should consider for a career.

Many school counselors don't seem to realize that scientific careers are open to Negroes, career days often don't bring black professional people to talk with the students, and job fairs sometimes fail to point out that professional careers are open to young blacks. The young Negro is seldom presented with the idea that there are Negro scientists he can look up to as models; textbooks seldom mention them. The eminent blacks who are held up as models for the young are chiefly celebrities from the world of entertainment or sports.

The preparation of the black student for a career in biology should be exactly the same as that of the white student. The subjects he should study, the diligence he should show, and the standards required of him to compete for jobs, do not differ in any respect from those outlined throughout this book. By and large, scientists tend to be more fair-minded than many other people, and the careers of those scientists with dark skins who have made enviable reputations prove that opportunities are available.

CHAPTER 2

ATTRIBUTES OF A BIOLOGIST

ONE FREQUENTLY HEARS a biologist—or some other scientist—marvel at his good luck in getting paid for something which is so much fun to do and which he says he would be doing even if he no longer had to work for a living. Science is a way of life, and scientists in general are happy, well-adjusted people. Motivation for following science as a career comes from within, and for many the urge to pursue science is as strong as an urge toward a religious calling. And like the religious calling, the chief attraction to science is neither monetary reward nor the promise of easy living. The realization that you can leave the world richer than you found it will be part of your reward as a scientist.

There is confusion in the minds of many people—and for that matter, in the minds of some scientists—of the distinction between science on the one hand and technology and invention on the other. The confusion is understandable. We are accustomed to frequent changes in our way of life brought about by new discoveries and inventions; new drugs provide ways of controlling diseases and prolonging life, new varieties of plants and animals increase agricultural yields, new processing and preserving methods bring us new foods (sometimes with improved taste or nutritional value), transportation is continually being speeded up, progress in the conquest of space is announced at almost weekly intervals—the list could be continued at great length. All these and more are listed as "advances of science," and many people believe that invention is the object of science. That is not really true, even though many inventions would not be possible without the scientific discoveries upon which they are based. Many very fine inventors are not scientists at all, while most scientists have never invented anything of practical value.

There is, then a distinction between science and technology or invention. Science is interested in understanding the forces of nature, and the scientist's reward is the joy of discovery and his contribution to knowledge. Technology, on the other hand, seeks to put discoveries to practical use. In some instances the distinction becomes somewhat subtle, and there are endless arguments about whether a scientifically trained person is truly a scientist if he uses his talents for making discoveries which he hopes will have a practical application. So we sometimes hear about *pure* or *basic* research as distinguished from *applied* research. Wherever one wishes to draw the line, there is no question but that a basic investigation often leads to a practical result. When the British biologist, Alexander Fleming, discovered that a substance produced by the bread mold *Penicillium* could kill bacteria, he was engaged in basic research, but in the end his inquiry led to the extremely important practical result of the isolation of penicillin. This work ushered in a whole new era in medicine—the antibiotic era. Penicillin would not have become a useful product, however, without a large amount of practical research and the application of skilled technology. Hence, science and technology often work closely together, and enlightened industrial leaders have dedicated more and more of their funds to basic science. Today, much important basic work in the life sciences as well as in other sciences, is performed in the laboratories of industry.

Science, and especially biological science, has much to contribute to social welfare, even though its *immediate* aim is not usefulness—any more than is a painting or musical composition. Some of the most important things that science has to contribute are the spirit of inquiry, the enthusiasm for exploration, the habit of rigorous analysis, the inquisitive outlook, the quest for truth, and the willingness to discard pet notions once they are found to be mistaken. To paraphrase John Playfair, the scientific approach is not desiccated and inhuman, but it is the most liberated state of mind known short of drug-induced anarchy.

The state of mind which I have just described is all too infrequent among people in most walks of life, but becomes "second nature" to one who has seriously studied science. As the biologist Conrad Lorenz has put it, it is a good morning's exercise for a person in research to discard a pet hypothesis every day before breakfast; it helps to keep him young. Such a change of mind would be very disturbing to the average adult. Since scientists are only human, it sometimes takes considerable courage for them also to publish retractions of their previous views; such retractions, however, can be seen from time to time in the biological literature.

Another distinguishing feature of the scientist is that he doesn't have to pretend to know something in his field that he doesn't know. He should have ideas of how to go about finding an answer to a question, and he may guess what the answer will be, but if he doesn't know, it is not shameful for him to say so. One of the first large scientific gatherings I ever attended was addressed by the then president of the American Association for the Advancement of Science who discussed freely a difference of opinion between himself and another eminent worker in the same field. He ended the discussion by saying, "Of one thing I am quite sure; neither of us knows anything about it." In a paper which appeared in the *American Scientist* in 1968, Louis B. Flexner said, ". . . although I have confidence in the observations, I am far from wedded to the interpretations, which, in my opinion, badly need further work to test them." How different this attitude is than that which is typical of many fields!

If you choose a career in the life sciences, you will find the "scientific approach" just described to be applicable, whether your interest lies in research, teaching, or any other activity. Experimental research, especially in the biomedical sciences, has a certain glamorous appeal to it, and some discussions of careers in bioscience (and other sciences) tend to equate science and experimentation. This is as erroneous as the impression of some 19th Century philosophers that science is nothing more than observation and classification. All aspects of science are important.

The same qualities of enthusiasm, careful analysis, quest for truth, and open-mindedness apply when the researcher observes, analyzes and interprets an "experiment" which nature has conducted as when the experimenter has performed the experiment. And need it be added that the teacher will be successful just to the degree he (or she) exhibits these same qualities? The worker engaged in laboratory testing, or in the applications of biology to the control of quality in industry, the administrator and manager of biological laboratories whether in research or production—each needs to keep these principles in mind and to appreciate the importance of his contribution to society.

The personal qualities which improve one's chances for success in biology are, by and large, those desirable in any scientist, with a few especially applicable to biology. This does not mean that all biologists have to fit a pattern or that all biologists are alike. Biology is probably the most varied of all the sciences and is broad enough to challenge anybody possessing curiosity about the nature of the world and of its life.

ENTHUSIASM

THE PERSONAL ATTRIBUTE which heads most lists of desirable traits for scientists is a genuine liking for the subject. Do you enjoy studying biology in high school? Do you like to read about science in magazines and newspapers? Have you ever made a collection of "nature" objects or made a special study of any group of living creatures, such as flowers, trees, butterflies, seashells, or what not? Do you like to attend scientific exhibits, or have you ever taken part in a science show? Do you find the performance of laboratory experiments an absorbing interest? Do you like to work with animals or with plants? If you can answer most of these questions with a "yes," you may have one of the most important qualifications for success in a biological career.

INTELLIGENCE

DON'T LET THE heading of this paragraph give you the wrong idea that only those of extraordinary intelligence can be good biologists. Emphatically, one does not have to be a genius to succeed in science; the Einsteins and the Pasteurs are few and far between. People with an extremely wide range of talents can find a place in the life sciences. As in any field of endeavor, of course, those with keen mental alertness and better-than-average intelligence stand a better chance of getting to the top.

The ability to reason both abstractly and concretely—that is, to solve problems, such as algebraic equations and also to understand the significance of new observations—will be useful, especially in research. When new facts are presented, one should have the ability to fit them in with things already known. At times, the new facts upset one's previous prejudices and notions; the biologist must be prepared to adjust his thinking accordingly. This capacity for intellectual growth is probably more important than is the possession of a high degree of "native intelligence" (whatever that is) to start with.

CURIOSITY

OTHERS WHO HAVE thought about the personal attributes of biologists have all given a prominent place to curiosity. The American Institute of Biological Sciences puts it as follows: "This inquisitive outlook, this penetrating quest for the truth, is the most distinguishing chararceristic of all biologists."

Advances in science have been made by those who *wondered* about things. This attribute is especially important for those who will enter biological research, but surely is not out of place even in the performance of routine lab or field work. In addition for the teacher of biology, the ability to foster an inquiring state of mind in one's pupils is a precious asset. If you wish to seek new frontiers of knowledge, there is no subject which will give you more satisfaction than biology. The quest for new knowledge takes biologists all over the world, from the icebound continent of Antarctica to the steaming jungles of tropical islands, and from the tops of mountains to the floors of the deepest seas. Biologists are also in the forefront of the space program, and in many laboratories devoted to the conquest of disease—and even delving into the nature of life itself.

OPEN-MINDEDNESS

WE HAVE ALREADY pointed out that a good biologist is willing to discard an old notion if it does not fit newly discovered facts. This is such an important qualification that it warrants having a section of its own in the present list. It should be made clear that there is a difference between being open-minded and in being vacillating; one should not be blown about by every change in the wind. Moreover it is the *interpretation* that changes, not the facts themselves. An observation made with sufficient care should be valid indefinitely, but the things seen by an observer may change with alterations—often very subtle and ill-defined alterations—in the conditions under which an observation was made. As the famous physiologist, Dr. A. J. Carlson (known affectionately to his friends and pupils as "Ajax") used to say: "Vot iss de effidence?" A good biologist forms his opinions, not on the basis of preconceived notions, but on observed facts.

PRECISION

IT WILL BE useful to many biologists to be able to make observations with great accuracy, and to detect minute differences between objects or events. Two kinds of plants or two kinds of insects may look so much alike that the untrained observer would think they were the same, though they may be different species; that is, so different that they cannot interbreed. It may be equally important to recognize similarities. Small differences may also be important in laboratory results. If you feel that you can not make such fine distinctions, it may be because you have never been called upon to do so; the ability to make accurate observations is a quality that can be learned, and every serious student of biology receives training in it.

PATIENCE

WHEN THE GREAT German biologist, Paul Ehrlich, sought to find a chemical compound which would destroy the parasite *Treponema* without killing the patient, he finally found a useful substance after trying 606 different substances. Although "606" has been long since superceded by better and safer remedies, its discovery was an important milestone in the history of biomedical science, for it initated the era of *chemotherapy;* that is, the treatment of infectious diseases with chemical compounds. Up to that time, the only agent that could be classified as "chemotherapeutic" was the ancient remedy quinine which was extracted from the bark of a tree—cinchona —and used to kill malaria parasites. In that prechemotherapeutic age, Oliver Wendell Holmes, a physician as well as a poet, told the Massachusetts Medical Society: "If the whole *materia medica* as now used could be sunk to the bottom of the sea, it would be all the better for mankind—and all the worse for the fishes."

If Ehrlich and his assistants had lacked patience, they might have said, "We will try 600 substances and if none of them work, we'll give up." This great advance then would have had to await the appearance of a more patient investigator. Actually, Ehrlich was extraordinarily lucky, for most modern drugs are selected after trials of many thousands of substances. One of the modern antibiotics, terramycin, for example, was found only after the study of nearly 100,000 molds!

It is true not only in the field of drug therapy but in nearly all biology that most trails lead nowhere. One doesn't know that a trail is a blind alley until it has been explored, so he must follow a path for a while, then start all over again. Often the same manipulations and observations must be repeated over and over again with a minor modification each time until the true path is found. It is not commonly appreciated by the general public that success is the exception rather than the rule, and that there is a great deal of trial and error associated with every great discovery. But most investigators take keen pleasure in the pursuit of knowledge and the joy of discovery—whether in the laboratory, the field, the classroom, or elsewhere—which more than compensates for the long period of testing and measuring and repeating that goes on beforehand.

OTHER PERSONAL ATTRIBUTES

THE LIST OF desirable attributes could be continued until it included everything we admire in people. There are, however, certain qualities which are especially helpful in particular kinds of jobs. Most biologists will need to exhibit a willingness to work with others and a genuine liking for people. These attributes are obviously desirable for teachers, but are usually an asset in other kinds of work as well, for the days of the "lone wolf" are pretty much in the past. Most work today is done in cooperation with others. In some types of laboratory work manual dexterity would be a valuable asset, particularly when one must manipulate very small objects. The degree to which this is required varies greatly among different types of biological jobs.

Writing and speaking ability will help not only teachers but others as well. The higher one advances, the more important it becomes to be able to communicate with fellow scientists. A biologist obtains an enviable reputation only if his fellow scientists understand what he is doing, and this is communicated in the form of papers published in professional journals and in lectures at meetings and conventions. To a considerable degree, an aptitude for speaking and writing can be learned by study and practice, so you should not be discouraged if you feel that you lack this aptitude. For that matter, there are many very fine jobs in bioscience that do not require public speaking or writing, but generally these are not the top grade jobs in teaching, research, or administration.

Certain specialized attributes will be helpful in specific types of jobs. For example, some of the duties of the wildlife biologist may require considerable physical stamina and strength, with some competence in outdoor craft. Arduous outdoor activity, sometimes in remote areas, may be required. On the other hand, there are laboratory and office jobs in wildlife biology, too.

If you feel that you have or can acquire many of the attributes listed in this chapter, and you are willing to work faithfully, you should be able to succeed in a biological career and find immense joy and satisfaction in it. Since some of these attributes are somewhat special—particularly enthusiasm for the subject, curiosity, open-mindedness, and patience—it is no wonder that there is a shortage of biological scientists. Perhaps you feel uncertain as to whether you possess the requisite attributes or not; this should encourage you, for if you'll review the list above, you may notice that by and large they are attributes toward which anybody can aspire. If you do decide to follow a career in biology, you will find that the rewards are great.

CHAPTER 3

EDUCATION OF A BIOLOGIST

FOR ALL PRACTICAL purposes there are no openings in biology for anyone who has not finished at least two years of college and who has not had some biology courses. Most laboratory technican jobs require such a high degree of understanding of the nature of the work that even the best high school education is considered to be insufficient, and most biologists prefer college graduates as technicians. A laboratory technician assists the professional biologist in performing experiments and in other duties, but rarely assumes charge of a project or does independent work without supervision..

If you are considering a career in biology, then, it is clear that you will need education beyond the high school level. How much beyond? That depends upon what place you wish eventually to assume on the biological team. There are schools which take high school graduates and train them in a couple of years to be laboratory technicians. Their graduates have no trouble obtaining jobs and they get good pay. They work in doctor's offices, hospital laboratories, or in various research centers, such as research foundations or drug companies. These technical jobs do not ordinarily lead to full professional status, and there is little opportunity for advancement unless further education is obtained.

It is not unusual for a young college graduate to accept a job as technician with the intention of continuing his education as time permits, and earning credits toward an advanced degree. This may be done by part-time schooling or by alternately working and studying full time. Some employers, especially industrial laboratories and some government departments, encourage employees to improve their education by permitting time off for class attendance and by paying tuition bills.

For the most challenging and exciting jobs in biology, schooling beyond the college level is necessary. After four years of college, the student receives a baccalaureate degree, which may be followed by a Master's degree after one or two more years of study. At least an additional two or three years are then required to obtain the highest degree, the doctorate. As we have seen, jobs as laboratory technicians are available to the holders of the baccalaureate degree. If one wishes to teach in elementary school or high school, the Master's degree offers an additional advantage, but for teaching biology in a college or university or for the best jobs in industry, government laboratories, and in most research institutions, the doctorate must be one's goal. In many graduate schools, the young biologist may enter upon a training program for the doctorate after obtaining the Bachelor's degree without bothering with the intermediate Master's degree. With good fortune, the doctorate can sometimes be earned within three years after graduating from college, but the typical graduate student in bioscience receives the Ph.D. at the age of 31, seven years after the B.A.; in the meantime, he has had three years of professional experience.*

---

* "Careers of Ph.D.'s in the Biosciences," by J. G. Creager and L. R. Harmon, *BioScience*, October, 1969, vol. 19, p. 910.

This may seem like a long and discouraging prospect, but remember that during all those years you will be learning things that are beyond anything you have dreamed of, that if need be you can be earning while learning, and that in the end you will find rewards beyond your present imagining.

HIGH SCHOOL SUBJECTS

IT HAS BEEN said that the scientist speaks with three kinds of languages: English, mathematics, and foreign languages. High school is not too soon to start the mastery of all three. English is the language you will be using to communicate with your fellow students and with your fellow scientists; you should strive to speak and write it correctly, concisely, and with the precise meaning you wish to convey. Unfortunately, many scientists are deficient in this regard. Editors of scientific journals frequently complain about the quality of the writing in papers submitted to them for publication. If you can learn to speak and write clearly, you will find your path smoother no matter in which direction you wish to go. Your colleagues will appreciate and respect your ability to communicate. So study as much English as possible, work hard on composition, and read, read, read.

The use of mathematics varies greatly among the various fields of biology, but more and more research biologists need to know the calculus and statistics, at least. For some of the newer fields of research, such as molecular biology and biophysics, more advanced mathematics is required; the mathematics requirement is more fully discussed in the next section of this chapter.

Science knows no international boundaries, and much of importance to biologists is published in languages other than English. At international gatherings of biologists, it is necessary to communicate with people who speak other languages. For these reasons, certain language requirements have been established which the student must fulfill before he obtains a degree in college with a major in biology or other science; there are special requirements for advanced degrees. The high school student should anticipate these requirements and start language study as early as possible. For advanced degrees, two languages are usually required. One plan a high school student could follow would be to study one modern language for three or four years in high school, then switch to a second language in college.

In former years, all high school students planning to go to college took two or more years of Latin in addition to a modern language. This course still has much to recommend it, especially for the student of biology. Not only is Latin used for many biological terms, but there is probably no single subject that can of greater help to the student in mastering his own language and in obtaining insight into other European languages.

In addition to English, mathematics, and language, the high school student interested in any science should include chemistry, physics, and biology in his program. With these studies, together with the basic requirements for graduation, the student will enter college well prepared to pursue any course of study. If after discussing your plans with your guidance counselor you feel unsure whether you wish to prepare for a career in biology, you should not feel discouraged. It is the exception rather than the rule for a student at the beginning of his college years to be certain what his future will be, and many young people discover new interests after they have been in college for one or two years and change their career goals then or even later. If you have a proper foundation of knowledge in English, mathematics, languages, science, and the humanities, you are prepared to undertake a study of any field of endeavor.

COLLEGE REQUIREMENTS

THE CHOICE OF a college presents no unusual difficulties for the young person intending to study biology. All—or nearly all—of the better colleges have departments of biology that range from adequate to excellent. In most instances the choice of a college for undergraduate study may safely be made on grounds other than the size or research reputation of the biology department. Of course, the biology department of the chosen college should be able to present a good solid major in biology; one way to judge its adequacy is to inquire whether the graduates of the department have been accepted in programs for advanced degrees at outstanding universities.

I cannot emphasize too strongly that you should not feel impelled to consider only Ivy League colleges, or others of similar age or social standing. They are fine schools, and their reputation for excellence has been well earned, but they do not have the monopoly on academic achievement that some status-conscious but ill-informed people may believe. Many of the outstanding biologists of recent years were graduated from colleges that are little known to the general public outside of their nearby communities. These colleges are widely dispersed geographically, and there is no one section of the country that can claim an outstanding advantage. Indeed, several surveys have been made of the academic origins of scientists. The surprising finding is that the small colleges of liberal arts that are scattered in such profusion throughout the country contribute a disproportionately large number of biologists and other scientists. A complete list of colleges offering biological training has been compiled by the AIBS and published as *Directory of BioScience Departments in the United States and Canada.**

---

* Van Nostrand Reinhold Co., New York. (a new edition is planned for publication in 1970 or 1971).

In your preparation for a career in biology, you will continue in college many of the subjects which you studied in high school. You will be able to plan your course of study according to your individual needs and preferences; you may have a member of the faculty assigned as your specific advisor. In this chapter we can give you no more than a few general statements about the kinds of studies you will need. During the first two years, most students will take courses in a wide variety of subjects to obtain a broad education. In the last two years, he will specialize more and more in the major field, with a somewhat less thorough specialization in another (usually related) field called the "minor." Most biology majors have "minored" in chemistry, mathematics, or physics, though in recent years some have minored in anthropology, sociology, or psychology.

The specific courses in bioscience which a biology major will take may vary greatly depending upon which branch of biology he will eventually choose, and upon those offered by the college. Generally speaking, the larger colleges offer a greater variety of courses. In some instances there may be separate majors of animal biology, plant biology, microbiology, etc. For most students, it would be unwise to specialize too strongly at an early stage. As the AIBS puts it: "Give yourself a chance to understand the breadth of biology before you concentrate on the blood flow in the muscles of a frog's leg." Most biology majors will want to have an understanding of general biology, know something about cellular biology, study the fascinating facts of heredity (genetics), learn how the organs function (physiology), obtain some knowledge of systematics and ecology, and find out what is known about the changes which occur with the passage of many generations (evolution). Other subjects that might be of interest include comparative anatomy, embryology, and microbiology. The student may not take a specific course in each one of these subjects, but he should become aware of the general principles of all of them, regardless of what biological specialty he eventually settles upon.

A thorough understanding of biology requires some knowledge of other sciences, though the degree to which other sciences are applied to biology varies enormously with the biological specialty. All biologists need college courses in general chemistry, organic chemistry, usually biochemistry, and in some cases physical chemistry. Most bioscientists recommend at least one course in college physics, and some recommend psychology as well. The details of planning one's course can best be left for decision after a year or two of college. A detailed study of educational requirements for biologists has been made by the Commission of Undergraduate Education in the Biological Sciences (CUEBS), and published in the *CUEBS Publication Series.**

A special study of the courses in mathematics needed by life scientists and other scientists was undertaken by a group bearing the mouth-filling name of National Study of Mathematics Requirements for Scientists and Engineers (NSMRSE). The most readable summary of their conclusions as applied to biologists appeared in *BioScience,* June, 1968. Some of the findings of this study were quite intriguing. Some very eminent biologists in certain fields—notably anatomy, botany, and zoology—admitted that they make very little use of mathematics in their regular work, and expressed the view that there is room in their specialties for scientists without much mathematical ability who are otherwise qualified. Yet, even in these specialties nearly all the actively working bioscientists recommended that students take first year college math, one year of college calculus, and a course in applied statistics.

While you are still in the stage of planning your career, and not even sure whether you wish to be a biologist or not, it is too

---

* Information about CUEBS can be obtained by addressing the Office of Biological Education, AIBS, 3900 Wisconsin Ave., N.W., Washington, D.C. 20016

early to know which biological specialty or discipline you prefer. It is, however, probably not too early for you to understand that biology is not just one science but a diversified group of related sciences. The educational requirements will vary accordingly; in mathematics, for example, the range is all the way from the modest demands we have just mentioned up to such specialties as biophysics for which some would recommend as many as ten courses in college math.

One might think that certain careers in applied biology, such as wildlife conservation, for example, might not require much in the way of nonbiological sciences, but the Professional Training Committee of the Wildlife Society recommends "a minimum of 15 semester hours in at least two sciences, such as chemistry, physics, mathematics, soils, or geology." Fifteen semester hours of college credit can be obtained in classes meeting one hour a day for five days a week for three semesters. Most biological specialties would require far more than that in other sciences.

In order to establish himself as a candidate for the doctorate, the student must demonstrate an ability to read biological literature in two foreign languages. Although this requirement can be met by considerably less knowledge of the language than is necessary for fluency in speaking, reading, or writing, the student will be well advised to study two languages as early as possible. If study of one language is postponed, for example, until graduate school, the time required for obtaining the advanced degree may be prolonged. Traditionally, the languages required of advanced students are German and French. In some schools and in some special fields, some other language (Russian or Spanish, for example) may be substituted for one of the traditional tongues.

In recent years, there have been increasing numbers of international meetings attended by biologists from many countries. Although most of these people speak English (with varying degrees of proficiency) and the majority of the talks at such meetings are in the English language (all educated continental Europeans seem to be better linguists than the average educated American or Britisher) anyone attending such a meeting will find it most profitable to possess more fluency in a foreign language than the minimum necessary for passing the usual college examinations. In some fields of biology, significant contributions to knowledge are appearing with increasing frequency in Spanish or Italian.

I would not want to close this discussion of the undergraduate education of a biologist by leaving the impression that the student need study only English composition, sciences, and languages. A biologist is a member of the intellectual community, and cannot properly fulfill his function in society—or even be a good biologist—unless he (or she) is an educated man (or woman). The young biologist should, therefore, take advantage of the opportunity to learn as much as possible about history, philosophy, economics, religion, the arts, or whatever liberal arts subjects most appeal to him or which his advisors recommend. In today's world, the truly educated man must have more than a little exposure to *both* science *and* the humanities.

GRADUATE STUDY

THE PRACTICE OF recognizing three levels of academic degrees—Bachelor's, Master's, and Doctor's—is an American peculiarity. In many foreign countries, there is no exact equivalent to the baccalaureate or Master's degrees, but the Doctor of Philosophy is universally recognized and respected as the highest official reward for the completion of a course of study aimed at the training of scholars, teachers, and research workers. In the United States, the requirements for the Ph.D. degree have changed little since Yale University inaugurated the Ph.D.

program in 1860. There are minor variations in the requirements from one university to another, but essentially they all include: (1) completion of certain prescribed courses, (2) fulfilling the language requirements discussed above, (3) writing a thesis which presents and discusses the results of the student's original research, and (4) passing special examinations, usually consisting of written examinations testing the student's broad knowledge of his subject, and a final oral examination centering upon the points covered by the thesis.

These sound like formidable requirements—and they are. But students of the biosciences are increasingly successful in satisfying them. In 1955-56, 1,025 doctoral degrees in the life sciences were awarded; by 1964-65 the number had increased to 1,928. The estimate for 1975 is 3,820 according to figures published in *The Random House Guide to Graduate Study in the Arts and Sciences*. In other words, the number about doubles each decade. In 1964, of the 1,251 Ph.D. degrees awarded in biology, 1,074 were earned by men and 177 by women. These young people were equipped, insofar as formal education could equip them, to obtain desirable employment at once, and ultimately to rise in their chosen profession as far as their abilities and achievements will carry them.

If this seems like a long and difficult path to you, be assured that it is really not as bad as it sounds, and probably no worse than you would need to follow in any other professional career. Excellence in any field is attained only by hard work and devotion. The musician must spend long years in practicing scales and exercises and in learning musical theory. The writer must labor diligently over his typewriter even when the muse seems to have forsaken him, and he must work all the harder when his efforts have been rejected by himself, his editors, or the readers. Success in business, too, comes usually only after many years of hard work, sometimes accompanied by disappointing setbacks, and the top business executive has usually spent his life in working long hours that make the traditional 40-hour week look like loafing by comparison. The difficulties in preparing for a career in biology are different, but they are not necessarily greater.

MEETING EDUCATIONAL COSTS

THE COST OF an education in biology at the undergraduate level does not differ essentially from the cost of any other college education at the same level. Those who elect to continue their education in graduate school will usually find no difficulty in achieving an earning-while-learning status.

It is difficult to generalize on the costs of a college education; not only do the costs vary greatly among different colleges and universities, but in the past several years they seem to have increased each year. The high school student should not wait until near his graduation to decide what kind of college he wants to attend, to take stock of his financial resources, and to examine the possibilities available in scholarships and loans to help defray expenses. The student should make full use of the information and help available from his high school guidance counselor and from other sources. When he applies for college entrance, he will find that he has plenty of competition, for there are 30,000 high schools in the country which supply about 2,000,000 applicants each year for college admission. Some colleges receive about ten times as many applicants as they can admit.

Much publicity has been given to figures like these, so some students get an exaggerated idea of the difficulties in being accepted in college. It is true that some of the "big name" schools will be able to accept only a fraction of their applicants, but on the other hand there are lesser known colleges which actually start the school year with vacancies in the freshman class. Some of these can offer a highly rewarding four years of college, with good training in selected fields—some of them in biological sciences—at costs appreciably lower than those of the "big name" schools.

The student who must adopt a minimal budget may attend one of the community colleges that are rapidly developing all over the country. Many of these offer no more than two years of work, so one must transfer to another college for the final two years. Attendance at a community college or at another college located within commuting distance of the student's home may eliminate one of the most expensive items of an education—board and room. The saving may amount to $1,000 or more a year, depending on the cost of commuting.

The Office of Biological Education of AIBS has aided in the development of a National Task Force of Two-Year College Biologists to increase the awareness of and involvement in professional activities by bioscientists in two-year colleges. This sort of cooperation and lively professional interest has aided in the development of biology in these schools to the point where some of them now offer programs in general biology comparable to (sometimes better than) those in the lower divisions of some four-year colleges. Other comments on two-year college biology will be found in Chapter 7.

Every state in the Union has one or more land-grant colleges or universities; altogether there are 67 of them. They originally received the designation as land-grant colleges from an Act introduced into Congress by Senator Morrill of Vermont and signed into law by President Lincoln in 1862. Each state carved out of the Northwest Territory, the Louisiana Purchase, and the territory purchased from Mexico was granted 30,000 acres of public land for each senator and representative of the state. The proceeds were earmarked for the establishment of "colleges of agriculture and the mechanic arts." Supplementary legislation has allowed all states to share in the federal funds. Most of these schools have become state universities, and they are able to offer a college education at a cost which may be on the order of $2,000 a year less than that prevailing at a private college of comparable eminence.

The land-grant colleges owe their very existence to developments in biological science. By the middle of the 19th Century the advances in zoology, botany, and physiology, as well as in chemistry, led to a demand for the establishment of schools for the study and promotion of scientific agriculture. The land-grant colleges were a direct response to this demand, and they were originally called "agricultural colleges"—sometimes irreverently referred to as "cow colleges." They were founded as centers of research in applied biology, and they traditionally have strong departments of biological sciences. Tuition rates are generally low, especially for state residents.

The student with limited financial resources can sometimes attend a more expensive school as easily as a land-grant college by the use of scholarship and loan funds. Such funds are increasingly available, and there are few students with good academic records and determination who need be denied higher education. The selection of recipients of scholarships is usually based on need as well as on past achievements, so most of the funds are reserved for those who need them most. Your guidance counselor has, or can obtain, full information on financial aids and the qualifications of applicants. For 50¢ you can obtain the publication *Financial Assistance for College Students* from the U. S. Government Printing Office, Washington, D.C. 20402. This guide lists financial assistance information supplied by colleges all over the country.

Most colleges have special loan funds administered by the college, and several organizations have established foundations which supply money for needy students. The National Defense Education Act provides money for colleges to loan to students; these loans bear no interest until one year after the student graduates or leaves school. Thereafter, nominal interest is charged, and 10 years allowed for repayment. Other loan funds also have liberal repayment provisions. Some religious denominations have considerable sums of money for lending to students of their faith attending colleges related to the church— and these include some excellent colleges.

Although many scholarships and loan funds are primarily available to students already in college who have demonstrated their fitness for the academic life, there are many for which the beginning student can qualify. Your guidance counselor can be of particular assistance to you in obtaining information about them. The initiative, however, must come from you, and it is your responsibility to fill out whatever application forms may be required, and to get them in *on time*. The same applies, of course, to fulfilling all the entrance requirements of any college.

The biology student is particularly fortunate in the number of part-time jobs available to him. In addition to the usual types of jobs which any college student may fill, some colleges employ students as part-time laboratory assistants. In some instances, the advanced biology student may even help out in the laboratory teaching of elementary courses. This provides valuable experience as well as a modest amount of financial aid. Part-time jobs are especially available at land-grant colleges. These colleges often operate agricultural experiment stations which provide both part-time jobs during the school year and full-time jobs in the summer. The young biologist may even be lucky enough to find employment in a particular branch of biology which will turn out to be his major interest in life.

A word of caution should be given here. During a student's first year it is advisable for him not to accept employment which will take more than a few hours a week during the school year. Many people find the transition from high school to college a difficult one. The work is demanding, and new study habits may have to be developed. While this personal adjustment is going on, the student must remember that his first duty is to his studies and some limitations should be placed upon extracurricular activities including employment. For this reason, some authorities believe that one entering his freshman year in college should have the full cost of the first year in sight before the start of the year, in the form of cash, expected help from family, scholarships, or loans, without needing to accept part-time employment. Such an arrangement is, no doubt, ideal, but not every beginning student can fulfill it.

Strange as it may seem, the financing of the graduate education leading to the doctoral degree is usually easier and simpler than that of the undergraduate years. Universities are eager to get talented graduate students for appointment as teaching assistants—or teaching fellows as they are often called. In return for their help in teaching laboratory work in beginning biology courses, teaching fellows receive cash stipends and often free tuition for their graduate studies. In the larger universities with numerous graduate students, so much of the teaching is done by teaching fellows that these universities are often criticized for lack of contact between the undergraduate student and the eminent professors who are listed in the university catalog as teachers.

Biological research at universities is often financed by grants of money from governmental agencies, private foundations, or industrial firms. A large share of these funds is used for fellowships and research assistantships for graduate students. There are many other types of fellowships, scholarships, and employment opportunities for graduate students—and even for their wives. They are so abundantly available that the American Society of Biological Chemists has stated: "financial aids to the graduate student in biochemistry are so numerous that no *talented* young man or woman is likely to be deprived of an opportunity to pursue graduate study." A similar statement could be made for many other biological disciplines. The Association of American

Colleges has summarized these opportunities in the publication *Fellowships in the Arts and Sciences.* The high school student, of course, need not be concerned with the details of financing graduate study, but it may be comforting to him to know that he need anticipate no great difficulty, if his college record is good.

CHAPTER 4

SOME BIOLOGICAL SPECIALTIES

THE VARIETY OF career choices available to the young person with a basic training in biology can scarcely be surpassed. We have already discussed this to some extent in Chapter 1, but it will be more apparent in the remarks which follow in this and succeeding chapters. No book the size of this one—and perhaps none written by a single individual—can really do justice to all possible careers in the large group of sciences collectively known as biology, or more accurately, as the biological sciences. But we shall do our best, so without further preliminaries let us discuss some of the individual kinds of careers open to biologists.

SYSTEMATIC BIOLOGY

ONE OF THE publications of the American Society of Zoologists divides basic biology into two categories: "descriptive biology" and "analytical biology." Although that publication does not define those terms, it indicates that descriptive biology "was predominant in the latter half of the 19th Century, when great collections were amassed and important museums were established" while analytical biology would include most of the biological research of today. That statement seems to imply that the *systematic biology* to be discussed in this section may be considered to be a part of descriptive biology and hopelessly out of date. I must take issue with any statement which tends to give an unfavorable image to systematic biology. I believe that we can show that systematic biology has a great deal of relevance to the present century, and offers attractive career opportunities to young people of today.

Systematic biology—also referred to as *systematics* or *biosystematics*—is a term often used interchangeably with *taxonomy,* though actually it is somewhat more inclusive than taxonomy. A taxonomist studies the appearance and structure of a plant or animal, determines how it differs from others, describes its surroundings, classifies it in its proper place within the plant or animal kingdom, and names it. The systematist does all these things, too, but in addition he may study the microscopic cell structure, the biochemical reactions taking place within the living tissue, the breeding behavior, the geographical relationships, the interplay between the organism and its environment (ecology), and any other data that may help to interpret the past, present, or future evolutionary history of the species. In short, the systematist is interested in any property of a species of plant or animal which distinguishes it from all other species. Thus, there is a continuity from descriptive taxonomy to the analysis of the evolutionary process, and only in its initial phases is systematics merely descriptive.

A career in systematics (or taxonomy) would have a special appeal to those who enjoy orderliness and who like to be independent—the rugged individualists. The taxonomist takes pride in bringing order out of chaos. His interests may be rather broad, so that he would be classed as a *plant taxonomist* (or systematist) or an *animal taxonomist* (or systematist), or even broader, a *general systematist.* On the other hand, he may specialize in certain groups of plants or animals; the number of such specialties is limited only by the number of groups of living organisms. It would extend this discussion unduly if we tried to list them all; a few examples will have to suffice. A systematic botanist, if specializing in trees, may be called a *dendrologist*. His colleague who concentrates on the smaller and simpler green plants, the algae, is an *algologist*. Another, fascinated by the yeasts, molds, and mushrooms is a *mycologist*. In many instances, an intimate knowledge of the characteristics and interrelationships of the various members of a group of plants is of great—or even critical—importance to agriculture or other economic pursuits.

The systematic zoologist (or animal systematist) has an equally interesting range of specialties from which to choose. The *entomologist* devotes his attention to insects, the *ornithologist* to birds, the *herpetologist* to reptiles and amphibians, the *ichthyologist* to the fishes, the *mammologist* to mammals, and so on through the long list of animal families, orders, classes, and phyla.

Generally speaking, there are few jobs specifically labeled herpetologist, ichthyologist, etc. Individuals with such specialized interests are *biologists* first of all, and they follow their specialty while teaching the usual biology courses. The American Society of Ichthyologists puts it this way: "Nobody is ever hired merely to teach ichthyology. . . . The young ichthyologist may . . . find that almost all of the available openings are for teachers of introductory courses like general biology." However, there are some exceptions to this. A limited number of openings for curators of ichthyology, or herpetology, or other specialties do occur from time to time—mainly in museums, zoos, aquariums, fisheries laboratories, and the like. Furthermore, a few specialties, such as entomology and mycology are so much in demand that we shall devote special sections of this chapter to them.

There are at least two great and compelling reasons for studying systematic biology. The first is related to the insatiable curiosity of the human mind; the mountain climber had to climb Mount Everest because "It is there." A great mountain of biological knowledge also "is there," awaiting discovery. The second is the urgent, and indeed critical, importance of a thorough understanding of biological interrelationships if our civilization is to survive. In this respect, systematic biology interacts with and overlaps other biological disciplines, especially *ecology* (the study of the interactions between organisms and their environment) and *genetics* (the study of heredity). The latter two disciplines are also discussed in this chapter.

Systematic biologists can take pride in past accomplishments and can thrill to the challenges of the future which only they can meet. These are of such importance that they deserve special consideration at this point. Most of us are aware of the fact that during the present century man's life expectancy has increased more than it had in all the thousands of years since the dawn of history. Our lives are not only longer but healthier. We are aware of the importance of medical research in this advance, but the contribution of systematic biologists to health and longevity is less well recognized. Taxonomists have studied and described the harmful bacteria, plants, and animals; they have determined their relationships to other organisms, including man; they have described the position which each species occupies in the natural scheme of things (i.e., their ecological niche). Without the foundation of basic knowledge provided by systematic biologists, the great advances in health science and medicine for which we are all so grateful would have been immensely more difficult if not impossible. This is true not only in the study of organisms likely to cause disease, but also in promoting the discovery of antibiotics, and of improved sources of essential nutrients including vitamins and proteins.

Malnutrition is a major problem in large areas of the world, and with increasing population it will become a bigger problem. In such areas, a cereal with increased protein content might make the difference between life and death for many people The interrelationships among various species of cereal grains established by the plant systematist supplies the background for the geneticist and the plant breeder to select the proper plants for hybridization for the production of new strains with the desired characteristics. These efforts have resulted within recent years in the development of the world's first man-made grain— a cross between wheat and rye, named triticale. Triticale resembles wheat but is much higher in protein content.

In the 1920's two systematic botanists spent two years in Asia. They spent $50,000 of American taxpayers' money, but brought back soybean types which now produce crops worth two and a half billion dollars annually to American farmers. Many plants and animals transported from one country to another prove to be valuable additions to the economy of the country into which they are introduced. Some of them, however, prove to be pests. An example of the latter is the prickly pear cactus in Australia. After it had ruined some 50 million acres of valuable grazing land, the help of the systematic biologist was sought in finding means of controlling the pest. An intensive study of all the information available on the prickly pear and on the plants and animals living in association with it revealed 160 different kinds of insects which were injurious to the cacti (50 of them were new to science). When some of these were introduced into Australia, one of them, a small moth from Uruguay, proved to be so damaging to the cacti that within seven years practically all the area formerly occupied by the prickly pear was reclaimed for grazing. This triumph for the systematists cost less than a million dollars, as compared to the estimated cost of eradication by spraying or by mechanical means of more than $500 million.

The outstanding success of American agriculture is based

upon the introduction of plants and animals native to other countries. No major crop and only one important domestic animal—the turkey—is indigenous to the United States. A program of research on the systematics of species of potential economic importance is necessary if further useful introductions are to be made. Only by learning as much as possible about the biology of foreign species can a scientific prediction be made as to whether a new plant might be useful, like the soybean, or a troublesome weed, like crabgrass; whether a foreign fish might be desirable like the brown trout, or undesirable like the German carp; whether an introduced bird will make an honored place for itself like the ring-necked pheasant, or will become a nuisance like the starling.

Many other examples of the usefulness of systematics could be cited, such as the identification of organisms in water to judge the degree of water pollution; the discovery of plant strains resistant to destructive diseases; the identification of fossil species of plants and animals in sedimentary rocks as an essential part of oil and mineral prospecting (does it surprise you that oil companies employ systematic biologists?), just to mention a few.

One project currently engaging the attention of ornithologists is a study of the birds of the Brazilian rain forest, with the aim of understanding how the birds there are involved in the transmission of diseases to other animals including man. These and other biological studies will be necessary before the full potential of the tropical jungles as habitats for modern man can be realized. A similar study of the birds of the islands of the Pacific Ocean is also under way.

There is scarcely any field of biology which offers such a wide variety of career opportunities. Systematics involves both field and laboratory work, and deals with all manner of terrestrial and aquatic habitats. Systematic biology offers opportunity for many to travel both in the civilized and the wild parts of the earth. The systematist can also relate his professional interests to many other technical and academic fields including even such nonscience subjects as history, logic, and classical languages.

Taxonomists (or systematists) find employment as teachers in secondary schools, colleges, universities, and agricultural colleges. Museums, botanical gardens, arboretums, zoos, aquariums, private research foundations, and various state and federal governmental agencies employ systematic biologists. The federal government has been employing them since the time of the Lewis and Clark Expedition in 1803-4. Most of them are in the Department of Agriculture or the Department of the Interior (see Chapter 7). Students in general have been impressed by the "glamour" of research in the health sciences to such a degree that relatively few have considered taxonomy as a potentially interesting and useful discipline. As a result, there is a serious shortage of systematic biologists, just at the time when a number of important national and international research programs relative to our environment are getting under way. According to Dr. R. S. Cowan, Director of the Museum of Natural History, Smithsonian Institution, there is an especially urgent need for taxonomists specializing in marine algae, soil organisms, and ethnobotany (systematic study of plants as related to human cultures).

The education of the systematist will follow the general course outlined in Chapter 3. To do his best work, he should be familiar with the comparative anatomy of a wide variety of organisms, not only those existing today, but those of past ages (paleobotany and paleozoology). He should understand genetics, ecology, physiology, biochemistry, and statistics. Courses in these subjects will be available in most undergraduate schools, although some of them may be taken while the student is working for an advanced degree. As in other biological disciplines, interesting and rewarding jobs will be available to the young man or woman holding a baccalaureate degree, but the possession of a doctorate will be necessary not only for the most complete understanding of the field, but also in obtaining the jobs with the highest rating.

ENTOMOLOGY

DURING PAST AGES, various forms of life predominated at different times. For example, during the Jurasic period some 150 million years ago, reptiles dominated the land, and we speak of the Age of Reptiles or of the Dinosaur Age. In like manner, we may consider our own time to be the Age of Mammals, but in another sense it could just as well be termed the Age of Insects. More than three-fourths of all the species of animals in the world today are insects or their close relatives. From the point of view of mankind, many are pests spreading disease or competing with us for food or destroying desirable plants, while others are useful pollinating trees, crops, and other plants or providing food for us or helping to destroy pest species. Whichever they do, they affect the lives of every person. *Entomologists* are the biologists who study them.

Entomology overlaps with many other biological disciplines. Although the description and classification of insect forms have been going on for more than a century, and hundreds of thousands of insects have been described and named, there is still much work left for the taxonomist. According to the Entomological Society of America there are large families of insects in which only about 10% of all the species are known. The identification and classification of insects are fundamental to all other research in entomology.

Those biologists who study the intimate nature of the physiological and biochemical reactions taking place within cells or even at the molecular level find that insects provide an abundance of useful and interesting material. The insect physiologist makes discoveries that are useful in many areas—sometimes even in human medicine. An important part of research in entomology is the study of insect control; that is, research aimed at reducing or eliminating the harm done by insect pests. Contributions to these problems are made by those in basic research and by those in applied research. The *economic entomologist* is especially concerned with reducing the damage done by insects to crops, forests, food in storage, and other interests of mankind. In the past, most attention has been paid to insect control by means of poisonous chemicals, so the work of the entomologist has overlapped that of the toxicologist. Beginnings have been made in the use of chemical substances other than systemic poisons; these might produce abnormal growth or behavior, they might attract insects to traps, they might render them sterile so that they can not reproduce. Research on the physiology, reproduction, and behavior of insects can contribute greatly to these goals; during the course of these investigations, knowledge is gained which may be of interest in other fields of animal and human physiology and behavior.

Still another avenue of approach to the control of insects is known as biological control. This involves the study of other insects which prey upon those we wish to destroy, and also knowledge of insect diseases—bacteria, viruses, or fungi which attack insects. The work of the entomologist thus may be closely linked with that of the microbiologist, the virologist, the mycologist, and so on. No form of life can be destroyed without affecting what is sometimes called "the balance of nature." The entomologist engaged in insect control will, therefore, have occasion to collaborate with the ecologist and the wildlife biologist.

It would be difficult to mention a field of biology offering a greater variety of employment opportunities than entomology.

One perpetually recurring demand is for teachers of entomology. Most entomology teachers will be employed in colleges and universities, including colleges of agriculture and veterinary medicine. Industries which hire entomologists include producers and processors of food, the chemical industry which produces chemicals for insect control, and the lumber and pulp industries which utilize the skills of forest entomologists. We see constant reminders to help prevent forest fires, but few seem to realize that insects destroy more timber each year than do forest fires.

Large numbers of entomologists are employed by state and federal governments. Some of these are in research laboratories. Some of them are engaged in biological survey work. Others are extension entomologists, helping farmers, growers, nurserymen, and householders with their problems of insect control in field crops, vegetable and flower plots and gardens, livestock, shade trees, or wherever insects present problems in every day living and commerce. Health agencies, state, national, and international, employ medical entomologists; that is, entomologists specializing in insects responsible for the spread of disease. Agricultural experiment stations, plant inspection agencies, mosquito control boards, conservation agencies, and museums are a few of the other sources of employment opportunities.

The preparation for a career in entomology is not markedly different from that outlined in Chapter 3 for biologists in general. Most entomologists will, of course, major in biology in college, although some universities offer a major in entomology. Specific courses in biology recommended by the Entomological Society of America include entomology, genetics, ecology, as well as the usual courses in general biology, cellular biology, and so on. In some branches of entomology, recommendations include parasitology, plant pathology, horticulture, agronomy, and animal science. The young entomologist should obtain knowledge of chemistry, physics, and mathematics, as well as the nonscience subjects, as discussed in Chapter 3. Entomology is one biological discipline in which there are many employment opportunities for those with a Bachelor's degree. These opportunities would include science teaching in secondary schools, employment with various state and federal agencies, and pest-control companies. For the top jobs in college teaching or research, the Ph.D. degree would be desirable and even necessary, just as with most other biological disciplines.

MICROBIOLOGY

THE AMERICAN SOCIETY for Microbiology was not exaggerating when it said recently, "microbiology is important from the core of the earth to the far reaches of outer space." Literally speaking, the word microbiology means the study of the very small—that is, organisms that can be seen only with the aid of a microscope. The biology of larger organisms is macrobiology. Microorganisms include bacteria, so bacteriology is a branch of microbiology. Many people think of bacteria as "disease germs" since so many infectious diseases are caused by bacteria. A closer look, however, reveals the fact that of about 1,500 known species of bacteria only about 100 cause disease. Many of the other 1,400 are of great importance to mankind, and we could not exist without their activities. They convert complex materials into simple substances, hence helping in the disposal of waste and in making the materials available for re-entry into the cycle of life. They fix nitrogen from the air; higher plants as well as bacteria use bacterially-fixed nitrogen for building proteins. In this way, much of the protein in our bodies comes directly or indirectly from bacterial action.

Microorganisms can be studied from the point of view of taxonomy, morphology, biochemistry, physiology, ecology, genetics, or any other aspect of living things, just as are higher plants and animals. Algae, fungi, yeasts, viruses, rickettsiae, and protozoa are among the kinds of organisms studied by micro-biologists. Most of these appear to be simple forms of plant life, some can not be readily classified as either plant or animal, while protozoa belong to the animal kingdom. A special branch of bioscience, *protozoology,* deals with the protozoa. A few protozoa, like some bacteria, cause disease—such ailments as malaria and amoebic dysentery.

The viruses defy simple classification as plants or animals, they are too small to be seen with an ordinary microscope or to be held back by bacteriological filters, but *virologists* have devised many ingenious ways of studying them. Viruses have so many unique features that some virologists consider their specialty as a separate science, and will hardly admit that virology is a branch of microbiology. The student of fungi is a *mycologist*—the word *mycology* comes from the Greek word for mushroom—and his specialty bridges the gap between microbiology and macrobiology. Fungi run the gamut in size from microscopic yeasts to huge puffball mushrooms. Mycology as a separate biological discipline is discussed in another section of this chapter.

Microbiology can boast some of the most illustrious names in the history of science and some of the greatest achievements for the benefit of mankind. Louis Pasteur, Robert Koch, Sir Alexander Fleming, and Jonas Salk are just a few of the great names that appear on the rolls of those who have contributed to microbiology. Within our century, a third of all the Nobel Prize awards in physiology and medicine have been bestowed upon microbiologists. Microbiology has so many practical applications that some microbiologists have complained that its value as a basic science has not been properly appreciated.

Microbiologists have been responsible for the development of vaccines, antiserums, and toxoids against a wide variety of diseases in man and animals. These include smallpox, typhoid fever, yellow fever, whooping cough, measles, influenza, and polio. Some microbiologists hope that some day the common cold, cancer, and others will be added to the list. In addition, microbiology has made many contributions not related to disease. Much of our knowledge of heredity was gained by studies on microorganisms. Many of our food and beverage products, including cheese, vinegar, wines and other alcoholic beverages, pickles, breads, olive and cabbage products, to name just a few, are dependent upon microorganisms, and microbiologists have contributed to the production and improvement of all of them. Microbiologists have also developed products for the preservation of meats, vegetables, and fish, and for the tenderizing of meats. Even the oil geologist utilizes microbiological information in his prospecting.

The education of the microbiologist should follow the general plan discussed in Chapter 3. The sciences studied during the undergraduate years will, of course, include general biology and genetics, and most students will major in biology, though some colleges permit a major in microbiology. Chemistry, both inorganic and organic, a basic course in physics, and mathematics through calculus and statistics are needed. Some of the other sciences may vary, depending upon what branch of microbiology the student elects for his specialty. It might be botany and plant pathology, for example, if he becomes interested in agricultural microbiology. If headed toward certain industries, one might include a course in chemical engineering. As in all biological sciences, employment is available for those with a baccalaureate degree. In fact, there is a strong and continuing demand for technicians in microbiology. The most responsible positions, however, will be filled by those with advanced degrees including the doctorate.

The microbiologist may obtain teaching jobs in high schools or colleges, or in many professional schools including medicine, dentistry, nursing, pharmacy, veterinary medicine, and agriculture. Private research foundations, government research laboratories, public health facilities, hospitals, and agricultural experiment stations employ large numbers of microbiologists. One of the newest fields of study is space microbiology. Microorganisms which are able to survive the extreme conditions known to exist outside our planet are being intensively studied, and when samples were brought back from the moon, microbiologists were among the first scientists to study them. The variety of jobs open in industry to microbiologists is too great to list. The food, chemical, and pharmaceutical industries employ large numbers of microbiologists in their research laboratories, in quality control, and in production. The large scale production of antibiotics and of steroids, for example, is practical only by the use of microorganisms. To produce these complicated chemical structures by the usual methods of synthetic chemistry would be prohibitively expensive, but the microbiologist can find organisms which produce enzymes or ferments which can do the job effectively and cheaply.

Other industries which use the skills of microbiologists include such varied specialties as wood products, paper, textiles, optical equipment, leather, and even electrical equipment. The products of all these industries are subject to microbial deterioration, and the microbiologist can forestall great economic losses by helping to control the deterioration of their wares.

In short, the man or woman trained in microbiology can have his (or her) choice of many varied careers.

GENETICS

A LONG-STANDING controversy has argued the question: are we what we are mainly because of our heredity or because of our environment? The science of genetics does not undertake to answer this question fully, but it does study the processes by which hereditary characteristics are handed down from parents to offspring. Simply defined, genetics is the science of heredity. Its pursuit involves observation of the superficial appearance of an animal or plant as related to its parents or its offspring, the inheritance of biochemical characteristics, the intimate nature of the structures in cells—especially the sex cells—which transmit heritable traits, and all other aspects of the complex mechanisms involved in heredity.

The work which individual geneticists do varies from the solution of highly abstract and theoretical problems to the application of genetic principles to practical and economically important subjects. Any species of plants, animal, or microorganism may serve as objects for the geneticist's scrutiny. Much of what is known about cellular mechanisms involved in the transmission of traits from one generation to another has been gathered from the study of relatively simple forms of life, such as bacteria and yeasts. The lowly fruitfly, *Drosophila,* has probably contributed more than any other animal to knowledge of the cellular structures known as chromosomes and genes which are involved in heredity. Among higher plants, probably more is known about the genetics of corn than of any other plant.

Human genetics has been widely studied, too, including hereditary traits, hereditary diseases, and the interrelationship between inherited characteristics and their modification by the environment. There are, however, many gaps in our knowledge. Much has been learned from the study of identical twins and their comparison with nonidentical (also known as fraternal) twins. Since identical twins develop from a single egg fertilized by a single sperm cell, they have the same genetic makeup. Nonidentical twins, on the other hand, are no more alike genetically than are ordinary brothers and sisters, since they develop from two eggs fertilized by two sperms.

Genetics has conferred many varied practical benefits upon mankind. The great hybrid corn industry, which has added millions of bushels to the annual crop of that important food, owes its existence to the study of the genetics of the corn plant. Recent developments in the genetics of rice give promise of similarly increasing the production of that staple food so important to the teeming millions of the Far East. Mention has already been made of the development of entirely new types of cereal grains, such as triticale, by collaboration between geneticists and biological systematists.

The selective breeding which has produced superior strains of livestock is a practical application of genetics. The genetics of fur bearing animals, especially the mink, has also been widely studied to the immense benefit of the profitable fur industry. Several years ago, a parasitic fly, the screw-worm fly, threatened to wipe out the cattle industry in Florida; the larva of this fly feeds upon the living tissues of cattle. Geneticists (and other biologists) virtually eliminated the fly from the entire cattle growing area by the simple expedient of releasing large numbers of male screw-worm flies which had been sterilized by radiation. Since the female screw-worm fly mates but once, a mating with a sterile male prevents the laying of fertile eggs. It does not necessarily follow that a similar treatment would eliminate all species of obnoxious insects, but a study of the biology, including the mechanisms of heredity, of all species would contribute greatly to the solution of problems presented by such pests.

Opportunities for additional contributions of genetics are abundant. Further improvements in food crops and in breeds of domestic animals will help solve food problems. Better knowledge of hereditary diseases is also needed. Genetic studies of endless variety are in progress. To present just one additional example: in another section of this chapter mention is made of the devastating effects of the chestnut blight fungus upon one of our most valuable forest trees. Recently, several thousand acres of an estate in Maryland have been dedicated to the genetic selection of blight-resistant chestnut trees, so that possibly once more one of the glories of the American forest may be seen.

Bioscientists specializing in genetics have no difficulty finding employment opportunities. In colleges and universities, most departments of biology, botany, zoology, and microbiology employ geneticists, and some universities have separate departments of genetics. Agricultural colleges employ theoretical geneticists as well as those concerned with practical applications in the management of livestock, poultry, or crops. In common with other biologists in colleges and universities, these geneticists usually spend part of their time teaching and part of it carrying out research programs. Many federal government laboratories employ geneticists; jobs are available in the Department of Agriculture, the Department of Health, Education, and Welfare, the Fish and Wildlife Service, the Atomic Energy Commission, and in other departments and bureaus. The laboratories of the National Institutes of Health, and the Brookhaven and Oak Ridge Laboratories have geneticists on their staffs.

Many states operate laboratories which employ geneticists, and for those interested in fundamental genetics research, employment opportunities exist in several privately endowed laboratories. Industrial concerns employing geneticists include pharmaceutical manufacturers, large producers of seed, especially hybrid seed corn, large producers of livestock and poultry, and large fur breeding farms.

The preparation for a career in genetics usually includes a college major in biology, followed by graduate study specializing in genetics. As with most biological disciplines, the most rewarding positions are available to those possessing an advanced degree, especially the doctorate. A background in physics, chemistry, and mathematics is very important (see Chapter 3). With the background thus obtained, together with a broad college educational program, the young man or woman interested in genetics will find no lack of opportunities for a successful and satisfying career.

ECOLOGY AND WILDLIFE BIOLOGY

TO MANY PEOPLE, ecology is a strange word. This is unfortunate, because ecology is the science which deals with the reactions between living things and their environment. With the vastly increasing impact that man makes upon his environment, it is important for his survival that he understands what he is doing to the world in which he lives. It is encouraging that within recent years there is some evidence that people are becoming more aware of the concepts of ecology; this was stated by Prince Bernhard of the Netherlands, President of the World Wildlife Fund as follows: "Ecology, in the next 10 or 20 years, may well become the most popular of the sciences—a household word to those masses who today are ignorant of both the word and its meaning."*

An amusing and classic description of the dependence of all species on each other originated with Charles Darwin and was later expanded by others. In the 19th Century, Britain was the world's greatest sea power. Darwin had noted that there were more bumblebee nests near towns and villages than farther out in the country. Bumblebees are important to the economy because they are the only insects with long tongues adapted to pollinate red clover. Field mice are enemies of bumblebees because they eat the combs and the bee larvae; the mice are relatively scarce around town because the cats which live in town destroy them. It follows, then, that without the cats, there would be less red clover in England. British cattle turned the red clover into beef, and bully beef was the staple diet of the British Navy. As the principle protectors of cats, the spinsters of England could be given credit for the dominance with which Britannia ruled the waves. This example may seem exaggerated, but on the other hand one can scarcely exaggerate the close

---

* In *Ecology*. LIFE Nature Library, Time, Inc., New York.

links that exist between the life of one species and that of all the rest.

Realization of the impact which human activities have upon the environment has been slow in coming; even now, the majority of people have no concept of it—and, sad to relate, an understanding of it is not universal even among biologists. Few of us realize what a late comer man is upon the earth. Paul B. Sears has pointed out that if the entire history of the earth were written in a book with each page recording a million years, we would have an immense volume of more than 4,000 pages. The beginnings of life would be recorded in the middle of the book, but man would not appear until the last page. The dim beginnings of agriculture would not be found until very nearly the end of the last line on the last page.*

It should be clear, then, that the "rules of the game" or what have been called the laws of nature became a fixed pattern long before man appeared on the scene. And there is nothing to suggest that man is exempt from the operation of those laws. The future of mankind upon this planet depends upon maintaining a balanced harmony with nature. Intelligent nonbiologists are beginning to understand these principles; Congressman Daddario, Chairman of the House Subcommittee on Science, Research, and Development, has stated that ecology "is not a matter of learning . . . it is a matter of survival."

The extinction of the dinosaurs was a very impressive event in geological history, but if we reflect that 1,000 species of dinosaurs became extinct over a period of a million years, we can see that on the average only one form disappeared in each 1,000 years. By contrast, man's activities have destroyed more than 200 species of birds and mammals within the past two or three centuries. Many others have been so drastically reduced in numbers that they may be doomed in spite of efforts to save

---

* "Beyond the Forest," Paul B. Sears, *American Scientist*, Autumn, 1967, vol. 55, p. 338.

them. It is not necessary to destroy the last member of a species in order to eliminate it, for there is a certain critical level below which a species fails to reproduce.

History is replete with examples, both ancient and modern, of adverse effect upon man himself when he flaunts the principles of ecology. Vast expanses of North Africa and of Asia that were once verdant grassland or woodland are now inhospitable wasteland, made so by overgrazing by man's domestic animals especially sheep and goats. The great Babylonian Empire once ruled all the Near East and the Nile Valley. Its economy was based upon irrigation in the valleys of the Tigris and Euphrates. But the irrigation water saturated only the top few inches or few feet of soil; as the hot sun evaporated the water from the surface, the water underneath rose by capillary action, carrying with it the salts picked up in the subsurface soil. As the water evaporated, this salt was left on the surface. Over many centuries, formerly fertile valleys were converted to salty desert which they remain to this day.

Within the present century, a similar decline in fertility and rise in saltiness of the soil has occurred in Egypt since the construction of the irrigation dam at Aswan in 1902. The new Aswan High Dam recently completed will add a million more acres for new irrigation projects. Some biologists believe that this may prove to be "the ultimate disaster" for Egypt. In addition to the threat of salinity to the fertility of the soil, the year-round irrigation ditches provide an ideal environment for a species of snail which harbors a parasite responsible for a debilitating and often fatal human disease known as schistosomiasis. In spite of many years of research, all attempts at controlling this disease have had no more than limited success, and increase in incidence of schistosomiasis has recently appeared in certain parts of the Nile valley.

Examples of the disastrous effects of man's interference with the balance of nature could fill a book much larger than this one. A public health team sprayed the thatched huts of a village with DDT to kill mosquitoes and flies. But the DDT also killed the wasps that preyed upon the caterpillars which ate the thatch of the roofs. Consequently, the roofs began to collapse. Not only that, but the small lizards which lived in the thatch and caught insects there absorbed so much DDT that the cats which kept the lizards from becoming too numerous died from a fatal dose of DDT from eating the lizards. After the cats died, the roofless huts swarmed with rats. The well-meant but ecologically careless efforts of the public health team led to greater problems for the natives than they had originally.

Modern farming practices, although temporarily improving crop yields, also present opportunities for future disasters. Heavy applications of nitrogen and phosphorous fertilizers have in many places polluted the water table which supplies wells and streams. This has already led to problems in the Great Lakes, especially in Lake Erie, where the increased concentration of chemical fertilizers has promoted the growth of certain types of bacteria and algae which are incompatible with desirable fish life, and a profitable fishing industry has suffered heavily. This, of course, was a type of pollution added to the already heavy pollution by commercial, industrial, and municipal wastes.

The environment was able to absorb everything that man could do to it so long as technology was in a relatively primitive state and man's numbers were not too great. But now it is threatened with a technology which includes the potentiality of destroying all life, and with an increase in the rate of population growth which if not curbed will render ineffective all other efforts at preservation of an environment in which most of us would like to live. As Dr. Vinzenz Ziswiler, of the Zoological Museum of the University of Zurich, has said, "The protection of nature must have the preservation of mankind as its ultimate end. . . . When man continues to destroy nature, he saws off the very branch on which he sits."

These are some of the problems to which the ecologist addresses himself. In recognition of their importance, some 55 nations have collaborated in establishing an International Biological Program. The research programs approved by the IBP are heavily oriented toward ecological problems. Increasing interest in ecology is also being shown in universities. For example, the University of Tennessee has recently established a new graduate program in ecology, an interdisciplinary approach involving the staff of half a dozen departments in the University and the Oak Ridge National Laboratory. Many other universities have established or are planning ecological institutes. A list of these can be obtained by writing to the Ecological Society of America (address is listed in the Appendix).

Biologists who become interested in ecology as a profession should have a thorough background in systematic biology, and should include both zoological and botanical subjects in their training. A study of wildlife biology may also be helpful. Among nonbiological sciences, in addition to the usual courses in chemistry, physics, and mathematics which all biology majors should have, a study of soil science and geology is recommended.

Teachers who are oriented toward ecology may find employment in secondary schools as well as collegiate institutions. University departments which hire ecologists include the usual bioscience departments—biology, botany, zoology, and microbiology—and also specialized departments, such as forestry, fisheries biology, horticulture, agronomy, entomology, oceanography, and wildlife management; there are also interdisciplinary programs. In the federal government the Forest Service, Soil Conservation Service, National Park Service, Fish and Wildlife Service, and U. S. Public Health Service are examples of agencies which utilize the skills of ecologists. The conservation departments of the various states also employ ecologists. The manufacturers of agricultural products, especially fertilizers and insecticides, hire ecologically oriented personnel, as do the members of the paper and oil industries where pollution is a problem. Several agencies of the United Nations have employed ecologists to gather data relating to the human environment in many parts of the world. Others have served as advisors.

From the description of ecology above, it should be clear that ecologists are vitally interested in conservation. Special careers are available in *wildlife conservation*; these are described in a publication by The Wildlife Society (see Appendix). The wildlife biologist aids in the management of game, fish, fowl, fur bearing animals, or any type of wildlife. He is interested in their habitats, and may be active in the preservation or restoration of streams, lakes, or marshes. Sometimes his work takes him into remote areas, often under rugged and difficult field conditions. Other wildlife biologists may work in laboratories, concentrate on teaching, take part in extension work, or write or give lectures about their specialty. The research that wildlife biologists do may be related to taxonomy, physiology, genetics, and many other fields as applied to wild animals, fish, or birds. The research may be of a basic scientific nature, or have practical applications.

The biologist who chooses to devote his time and talents to ecology and conservation will be rewarded not only by a fascinating study, but by the knowledge that his future and that of mankind are intimately bound together.

MARINE AND AQUATIC BIOLOGY

SOME BIOLOGISTS ESPECIALLY concern themselves with plants or animals which live in a watery environment. They may find fascination in a study of the classification, mode of life, functions, or adaptations of organisms inhabiting the sea (marine biology) or fresh water (aquatic biology). Few biologists will have interests broad enough to cover all these aspects thoroughly; one may be especially interested in the physiology of fishes, another in the systematics of marine algae, yet another in the structure or embryology of a particular group—for example, the minute invertebrate animals which form a part of the plankton (the small floating or swimming forms which are the basis of the food chain for all the larger creatures).

The economic importance of marine biology is being increasingly recognized. Most of us have read about the threat to the survival of mankind which has been posed by the often-mentioned "population explosion." Even the most optimistic predictions foresee serious food shortages in widespread areas of the earth within the next few decades, while some forecast world-wide famine. There is no question that population is increasing faster than agricultural production in the world as a whole. Marine biology may offer one bright spot in this gloomy picture, for the knowledge provided by a study of sea creatures has already helped to increase the world harvest of food from the sea. According to a recent estimate, this harvest is increasing at the rate of 8% per year. Food from aquatic and marine organisms contribute protein, vitamins, and minerals to human nutrition—the very essentials which people in underdeveloped countries need the most.

To realize the full potentialities of aquatic organisms, it is not enough to rely upon fisheries, but it will be as important to practice animal husbandry in the water as it is on the land—agriculture must be supplemented by aquaculture. It may surprise many readers to learn that aquaculture is already widely practiced in some countries. Indeed, a treatise on fish culture was written in China as long ago as 475 B.C. The species of aquatic and marine animals widely cultivated include several kinds of fish, such as salmon, trout, edible carp, catfish, and many others. The principal invertebrates widely cultured are oysters and shrimp.

The yields achieved in water far outstrip those on land. Fertilized catfish ponds in the southern part of our country may yield as high as 4,500 pounds of fish per acre per year. This figure is dwarfed by the crops harvested from salt water. Some figures quoted by workers in ocean research laboratories range from 51,000 pounds of meat per acre annually in Japanese oyster beds to the fantastic figure of 268,000 pounds per acre per year in Spanish mussel colonies. To give some idea of the meaning of these figures: a good yield of small grain on a farm may be 100 bushels per acre. At 60 pounds per bushel, this would be 6,000 pounds of grain per acre. When this is fed to animals for producing meat, it will yield about 600 pounds of unprocessed meat.

The full potentialities of aquaculture (sometimes referred to as mariculture when sea water is involved) can not be realized without the contributions to knowledge which only the biologist can supply. For example, the biosystematist could study the relationships among species concerned, and perhaps find useful species which are not yet used for food. The systematist would also be in position to study the many lowly members of the food chain, to provide most effectively the food for the species being cultivated. The systematist would also supply information to aid the geneticist in selecting species for hybridization. The geneticist would supervise selective breeding and hybridization. An active program of this type has been in progress for some years at the University of Washington in Seattle, using rainbow trout as subjects. The potentialities of this research are illustrated by the fact that these experiments have produced a breed of trout which grows to a weight of six to seven pounds within the length of time that a wild trout takes to reach six to seven ounces. These fish also tolerate water temperatures which the wild trout can not endure. The adaptation of creatures to their environment is the province of the ecologist. Subtle changes in temperature, salinity, and other properties of an aquatic environment can make great changes in its suitability for a given species.

There are many unsolved problems in aquaculture. For example, there seem to have been no experiments so far in genetics of oysters or shrimp. Studies of the physiology of many species, especially reproductive and endocrine physiology, need to be done. The results would aid in the control of spawning. Aquaculture is only a special application of marine biology and is by no means the only source of career opportunities in aquatic and marine biology. Departments of Oceanography in universities conduct studies in marine biology as well as in the chemistry, physics, and geology of the marine environment. The biologists in such departments are concerned with all aspects of the systematics, biochemistry, and physiology of plants and animals living in a watery environment. Many departments of botany and zoology also employ biologists interested in aquatic and marine organisms.

More than a score of universities offer advanced degrees in marine biology and fisheries (see *Lovejoy's College Guide*). Special laboratories devoted to research in marine biology are located on the Atlantic, Pacific, and Gulf coasts. Some are independent, such as the well-known Marine Biological Laboratory at Woods Hole, Massachusetts. Others are directly connected with universities, such as the Institute of Marine Science of the University of Miami and the Scripps Institute of Oceanography of the University of California at San Diego, or the Laboratory of Limnology of the University of Wisconsin (Note: Limnology is the scientific study of all aspects of bodies of fresh water, just as oceanography is the study of all aspects of the ocean.)

These institutions offer careers to biologists primarily interested in research; in those supported by universities there are ample opportunities for teaching, and positions are available for those who enjoy routine technical work, such as chemical analysis, plankton sampling, and the like. Ocean-going research vessels present especially interesting opportunities for a limited number of biologists. Such a vessel is the *Alpha Helix,* which has provided a floating laboratory in such places as New Guinea, the Galapagos Islands, the Great Barrier Reef of Australia, the Amazon River, and the Bering Sea. The Man-in-the-Sea Program of the U. S. Navy and similar projects also require marine biologists of various kinds, as well as physiologists.

Clearly, most of the career opportunities in marine and aquatic biology are available for those with advanced degrees, especially the doctorate. Laboratory positions of a relatively routine type can be filled by those with a baccalaureate degree in marine biology, fisheries biology, or limnology. Most aquatic biologists will have majored in biology, but in some places there are departments of marine biology and fisheries, or a department of oceanography.

Several commentators have urged that the exploration of the "inner space" of the earth's oceans be given a priority at least as great as the glamorous exploration of outer space of the moon, planets, and beyond. As the importance of knowledge of the seas becomes more widely recognized—and there are several lines of evidence that it is becoming so—career opportunities in marine science, both biological and physical, will continue to increase.

SOME SPECIALTIES IN PLANT SCIENCE

THERE ARE MANY varieties of botanists. They are the biologists who are especially interested in plants. *Plant systematists* or *taxonomists*, who have been discussed in a preceding section, describe, classify, and study the evolutionary interrelationships of the endless variety of members of the plant kingdom. *Plant morphologists* are fascinated by the form and structure of plants, *plant ecologists* with their environmental relationships. There are no hard and fast lines between these various specialties. It is clear that the systematist, for example, must have an understanding of morphology and ecology. *Plant physiologists* are primarily concerned with the normal functioning and behavior of plants, how the plant absorbs energy and what it does with it, for example. The highly important problems of plant disease engages the attention of the *phytopathologist* (or *plant pathologist*). Some botanists specialize in certain groups of plants, for example, the *bryologist* studies mosses and liverworts, and the *mycologist* concentrates his attention on fungi.

Other plant scientists use their training in practical applications of their skills; they may become foresters, horticulturists, agricultural scientists, and the like. Careers in botany, then, may be quite varied. A few of them will be considered in the following sections of this chapter and in Chapter 6.

PLANT PHYSIOLOGY

ONE COULD SCARCELY imagine a science of greater importance for mankind than plant physiology. This becomes apparent when one reflects upon the fact that all life upon earth, mankind included (but with the execption of a very few unusual forms of bacteria), relies upon the sun as its ultimate source of energy, and that all animal life—including mankind— is utterly dependent upon the physiological activities of plants to convert the sun's energy into a form which suits our own needs. This is done, of course, by photosynthesis, the process by which the pigments of plants, especially chlorophyll, absorb the energy of the sun's rays and use this energy to convert carbon dioxide from the air and water from the soil into sugar. The sugar may then be converted into starch or fat or other substances, and with the addition of nitrogen from the soil into protein. The products of these reactions are the basic ingredients for all the metabolic processes of our own bodies—the processes which enable us to exist.

The increasing population of the earth will make continually growing demands upon our ability to control the growth and development of plants for improved food production; the plant physiologist is one of the key men in this struggle. Among the discoveries of plant physiology which have already been of great value to mankind are those concerned with the chemical substances—plant hormones—which regulate growth, cell division, and the differentiation of the various organs of the plant, such as roots, leaves, and flowers. Some of these hormones, known as "auxins," are used for the rooting of cuttings, for the regulation of flowering and the setting of fruit, and for the destruction of weeds by the stimulation of abnormal overgrowth. Others, known as "gibberellins," produce spectacular effects upon flowering and upon rate of plant growth. A great deal more needs to be known about these substances and how they act. This is only a sample of the many unsolved problems of plant physiology. We also need a more thorough understanding of the mechanism of photosynthesis, for the chemist still cannot duplicate photosynthesis in the test tube. Valuable, too, would be a more complete knowledge of minerals absorbed from the soil and their functions within plants, and a fuller elucidation of the mechanisms of the utilization of water by plants, especially in those parts of the world where water is a precious commodity in short supply.

The solution of these unsolved problems relating to plant physiology will be sought by those plant physiologist who are engaged in basic research, but it must not be thought that basic research is the only occupation of plant physiologists. The American Society of Plant Physiologists (see Appendix) estimated that about two-thirds of the 3,000 plant physiologists active in 1968 were working in universities; most of these divided their time between teaching and research. The remainder were employed in government laboratories, in industry, or by private research foundations. Research in plant physiology was estimated to be about equally divided between basic and applied research. The plant physiologist interested in applied research finds many ways in which his chosen science is of practical benefit. If he is in industry, for example, he may help to develop new chemicals or new ways of using chemicals for controlling plant growth or for increasing crop production, or for destroying weeds.

Similar problems may also attract the attention of the practically-minded plant physiologist in a government laboratory, such as one of the laboratories of the U. S. Department of Agriculture or of one of the states. Many agricultural colleges provide opportunities for applied research in plant physiology in their departments of horticulture, agronomy, and others.

In preparing for a career in plant physiology, the student will usually complete an undergraduate major in biology, botany, or agriculture; he (or she) may find it useful to take an undergraduate course in plant physiology, but rarely will it be possible to major in it since plant physiology is primarily a subject for graduate study. The American Society of Plant Physiologists has estimated that 95% of all plant physiologists have a Ph.D. degree. The requirements for entry into graduate programs are set by each graduate department. In general, however, they include college mathematics through one year of calculus; chemistry including one year of organic chemistry; several courses in biology including general biology, genetics; and botany including plant structure and at least an elementary course in plant physiology. Biochemistry, cell biology, and ecology are also frequently recommended. These requirements differ only in certain details from those of other biological disciplines.

It may be seen that plant physiology forms a connecting

link between basic biological research on the one hand and agriculture, forestry, and similar applied disciplines on the other. The young man or woman trained in plant physiology will therefore find a variety of outlets for his (or her) talents, and will find a great, and increasing, demand for those skilled in this profession; there is no major university or agricultural research center that does not employ plant physiologists.

PLANT PATHOLOGY

CLOSELY ALLIED TO plant physiology is plant pathology (or phytopathology) which shares with its sister science the quality of being of supreme importance for the maintenance of our civilization. While the plant physiologist contributes discoveries which enable us to understand plant growth, development, and behavior, with corresponding improvements in food production, the plant pathologist provides knowledge which enables us to control the plant diseases which continually threaten to wipe out all the gains made by agriculture, horticulture, forestry, and similar disciplines.

The American Phytopathological Society has pointed out that without the work of the plant pathologist there would be little wheat grown in the Middle West or the Pacific Northwest, nor would sugar cane plantations flourish in the South, nor could the great fruit and vegetable industries survive. The threat of plant disease is not an idle one. Only a generation or so has passed since "rust" threatened to destroy the wheat growing industry of the U. S., and wheat rust still causes millions of dollars loss each year. A potato blight in the 1840's caused death by starvation of a quarter of a million people in Ireland, and was largely responsible for the mass migration of Irishmen to America. One of the most beautiful and useful trees of the original American forest was the chestnut; its fruit was a delicious nut, its wood was valuable for furniture and cabinetry, and its growth beautified the landscape. Within a couple of decades after the introduction of the chestnut blight fungus into this country, the American chestnut had almost completely disappeared. As this is being written, a similar fate is threatening the even more valuable oak trees, and many millions of our beautiful elms have been killed by the Dutch elm fungus.

These few examples serve to illustrate how plant diseases continually threaten to cause critical shortages of food, fiber, and building material. The near miracles wrought by plant pathologists in the past have not abolished the threats, and there remain challenges as great as or greater than any that have previously been met. The tools which will be employed for meeting those challenges will include the breeding of plants resistant to disease and the use of chemicals, including antibiotics and plant hormones for combating disease. The plant pathologist thus cooperates with the plant physiologist, the geneticist, the biochemist, and others in this exciting work. The American Phytopathological Society estimates that there are more than 50,000 destructive plant diseases; to combat these, there are about 2,600 plant pathologists in the United States. More are needed.

Phytopathologists find employment in many diverse areas. There are departments of plant pathology in more than 50 colleges and universities in the U. S. Many of these are in colleges of agriculture. Teachers trained in plant pathology are also employed in departments of biology, agriculture, and botany, as well as in extension courses, and sometimes in high school. Research positions are available in the agricultural experiment stations of all 50 states, as well as in the U. S. Department of Agriculture and some other government departments. All major industrial firms engaged in the production of agricultural chemicals employ plant pathologists. The federal government's program of technical aid to foreign nations engages many plant pathologists. Other phytopathologists work in conservation projects; these may be in wide open spaces, ranges, national parks, and forests, or in cities working with grasses, trees, flowers, and ornamental plants. In addition to all these sources of employment, a growing number of phytopathologists are becoming "free-lancers"; that is, they go into private practice as consultants on plant disease, or start up their own services for testing or disease control.

The educational preparation for a career in plant pathology is essentially the same as that already outlined for plant physiology. There are a few institutions which offer undergraduate majors in plant pathology. The graduate of such a program, possessing a Bachelor's degree, would find many interesting employment opportunities, chiefly with chemical companies, in some government agencies, and as science teachers in secondary schools. For most professional careers, however, the student must continue through graduate school and acquire the Ph.D. degree. Thus equipped with formal education, the young man or young woman will be in position to meet the important challenges posed by the diseases to which the members of the plant kingdom are heirs.

MYCOLOGY

IN A PRECEDING section on plant physiology, we mentioned the importance of plants in converting carbon dioxide and water into substances which supply energy to animals which eat the plants. A very large and important group of plants lack the green pigment, chlorophyll, necessary for this process of photosynthesis. These are the fungi. Like most bacteria and animals, fungi are obliged to live upon organic matter previously made by green plants. If they depend upon dead organic matter, they are called *saprophytes;* if upon living organisms, they are *parasites.* Perhaps the most familiar examples of the fungi are the mushrooms, but the fungi also include molds, mildews, yeasts, and the like. A student of fungi is a mycologist, a word derived from the Greek word for fungus.

These simple plants are of great importance in the scheme of nature, and in the economy of our civilization. Although a few of them cause disease in humans, the majority are of benefit. They take part in the breakdown of dead trees and other plants, helping to return the dead tissues to the soil and the air, thus completing the cycle of growth and decay. The by-products of these activities are widely used by man; they turn milk into cheese, sugars into alcohol; they produce medically useful steroids, such as cortisone, and antibiotics, such as penicillin, streptomycin, and many others. Fungi are abundant in the soil, on foods, in the air, on textiles and lumber—indeed, anywhere there is organic material and moisture. They are so widespread and their metabolic products are so useful that the discovery of new fungi and of new products made by fungi presents an exciting challenge for future mycologists; many mycologists believe that there are more fungi and more useful fungal products awaiting discovery than have yet been found.

This group of plants, then, presents many opportunities for the systematist or taxonomist who was discussed in a preceding section of this chapter; but it also has much to offer other biologists. Geneticists have learned much about heredity from studying the fungi. Cellular biologists and others have also made discoveries in studying the fungi which might have important bearing on the problems of cancer. In the applications of biology to forestry and to agriculture, the mycologist collaborates closely with the plant pathologist, for the fungi are the chief cause of disease in higher plants.

The above description of mycology makes it apparent that there are many kinds of opportunities open for the young man or woman skilled in this field. The importance of mycology is becoming increasingly recognized, and The Mycological Society of America (see Appendix) has recently pointed out that the demand for good teachers and research workers in mycology is increasing steadily. This is reflected in the fact that many colleges and universites are increasing their facilities for teaching mycology (and hence hiring more mycologists to teach it) and some are offering courses in mycology for the first time. In addition to other colleges and universities, certain specialty schools, such as medicine, forestry, and agriculture, utilize the skills of mycologists. Medical research laboratories in private research institutes, laboratories in the pharmaceutical industry, and installations of the public health service also offer opportunities. Other industries and laboratories employing mycologists include food production, leather, textiles, and forests.

The undergraduate training of the future mycologist will not differ markedly from that of other biologists, especially that of other botanists. Often, a specialization in mycology might not come until graduate school, although some undergraduate departments of biology do offer courses in mycology. The mycologist must have a background in biology in general, especially general botany. Microbiology, biochemistry, physiology, and genetics will also prove to be generally useful. In certain applications of mycology, specialized subjects, such as plant physiology, plant pathology, forestry, or others, will be useful. For full understanding of the field and for the best opportunities for advancement, the mycologist should aim for the Ph.D. degree, although during various stages of his progress he may find some rewarding employment opportunities before he has obtained the final degree.

CHAPTER 5

CAREERS IN APPLIED BIOLOGY: THE BIOMEDICAL SCIENCES

BIOLOGISTS WHO CHOOSE to work in one of the bio-medical sciences find themselves in the very forefront of advances in knowledge of health and disease, in factors governing aging, and in improvements in the physical and mental well being of their fellow men. Nearly all the advances in medicine have been based upon observations previously made in the laboratory of the bioscientist. The discoveries made in these laboratories have applications not only in medicine, but in many other fields of benefit to mankind.

PHYSIOLOGY

WE HAVE SPOKEN of biology as being not merely one science, but a group of sciences. This is well illustrated by physiology, which offers a variety of careers. Physiology is placed here in this chapter only for the convenience of the author. You should understand that physiology is a broad term, embracing the interests of all life scientists whose primary concern is with the processes that sustain life. The present discussion will be confined to animal physiology; plant physiology has been considered in the previous chapter.

The interests of physiologists are so varied that it is difficult to define physiology; it is usual to consider it as being the science concerned with the functions and operations of a living being or any of its parts, and of the interrelationship of one living part to another. The American Physiological Society issues career brochures not only on physiology as a whole, but several separate brochures for different areas of physiology (see Appendix).

Physiologists are concerned with such matters as: What makes animals (or people) grow? What regulates the rate at which they grow? How is food digested? What regulates the activities of the digestive tract and how can these activities be modified? How are the products of digestion absorbed into the blood stream, and then how are they distributed to the areas where they are needed? Why do we need blood and what governs its circulation? What are the intimate mechanisms involved in reproduction for the perpetuation of the species? The list of questions could be extended on and on. To find the answers, physiologists study living creatures, including man himself. Information gained by the study of animals most nearly resembling man—that is, the mammals—have the most obvious application to the problems of human physiology. In addition much is also learned from observations on creatures far removed from the human on the evolutionary scale.

A few examples will illustrate some of the things that have interested physiologists. One physiologist, for example, studied for many years the water balance in frogs; that is, the intake and output of water by the body of the animal. When research workers perform tests of this kind, others often inquire: of what practical use is such activity? To the scientist such a question may seem irrelevant, and the experiments may have been done simply as a response to the need of the human mind *to know.*

But in this instance, the simple experiments in the frogs were destined to lead in many directions. Other physiologists took up the study, and discovered that the electrical and chemical forces involved in the transport of water and salt through frog skin could also be involved in the functioning of the nerve cells and the kidneys in human beings. These investigations, in turn, were eventually, after many further steps, put to practical use by physicians wishing to regulate kidney output in patients with certain kinds of heart disease. But that is not all. The knowledge gained in these studies also proved to be invaluable in aiding men to cope with desert conditions, and much use was made of it in the desert campaigns in North Africa during World War II.

The migration and breeding cycles of migratory birds have long excited the curiosity of man, and they still present many unsolved problems. However one of the interesting facts that has been found is that one factor in some of the cyclic behavior of birds is the length of day. Light, and a specific number of hours of light during a single day, perceived by the visual apparatus of the bird triggers off the release of a chemical substance (a hormone) in a portion of the bird's brain called the hypothalamus. Cyclic behavior related to the time of year, and hence the length of day, is also characteristic of many other animals including some mammals. No one, however, seems to know whether a similar factor may be involved in the release of hormones in humans. Might this give a rational basis for the old adage, "In spring a young man's fancy lightly turns to thoughts of love?" And to what extent do we interfere with the natural cycle of hormonal events by artificial lighting?

A physiologist studying the flight muscles of a housefly might be thought to be engaged in a line of research having little relevance to human medicine. However a substance has been found in these tiny organs which is correlated with aging in the animal. With more and more people living into the retirement years, the processes involved in aging become of increasing importance. Although the studies on the flight muscles of the housefly have not yet led to any practical application in the treatment of the infirmities of old age in man, the continuity of life throughout the animal kingdom is such that no one can predict to what heights basic discoveries may lead, no matter how humble a creature may be the subject of inquiry.

Most physiologists specialize, and the list of specialties in physiology is a long one. Some are interested primarily in teaching, others mainly in research, while others might seek to apply physiological knowledge to some practical field, such as animal husbandry, or insect control, or veterinary medicine. The cellular physiologist is fascinated by the processes that go on within the microscopic world of individual cells. The cells may range all the way from bacterial cells to those derived from human tissues. Other physiologists may become engrossed in the functioning of some particular organ of the body or a whole system of organs. For example, a physiologist who studies the endocrine system of the body is called an endocrinologist. Even the endocrinologist may specialize and may study, for example, the reproductive system, thus becoming a reproductive physiologist. Some physiologists study particular groups of animals, such as insects, birds, fishes, or even protozoa. Perhaps you would find it interesting to learn more about the physiological impact of special environments, such as the tropics, the arctic, or space. It is not my intention to give an exhaustive list of the kinds of physiologists there are, but merely to indicate by a few examples the surprising diversity available to you if you are considering physiological science.

Many physiologists are employed in teaching in colleges and universities. Not all colleges, however, have separate departments of physiology; at the undergraduate level of teaching, most physiologists have appointments in departments of biology, zoology, entomology, and the like. Other educational facilities that employ large numbers of physiologists include medical, veterinary, and agricultural colleges. There is an especially brisk demand for physiologists in medical schools; in a very important way, physiology is the very foundation of medicine, and physiologists are employed not only in departments of physiology and other basic sciences, but often in clinical departments— medicine, surgery, etc.—as well. Other employers of physiologists include research laboratories connected with clinics and hospitals, private research foundations, drug companies, U. S. government laboratories and regulatory agencies, various laboratories concerned with marine biology or with life in fresh water.

According to information published by the American Physiological Society in 1965, only 16 colleges and universities in the United States offer a major in physiology leading to the A.B. or the B.S. degree. For the average student this is probably just as well, since he will not want to specialize too early. During the undergraduate years, the future physiologist will wish to acquire a general background in biology, physics, chemistry, mathematics, and other academic disciplines. A course in general physiology and one in biochemistry would be desirable, but many colleges do not offer separate courses in physiology, and many successful physiologists have had no physiological training during their undergraduate years other than that which is part of the subject content of other courses. Hence, for the majority of physiologists, specialization will come only in graduate school. A wide choice of graduate schools is available; the same American Physiological Society publication mentioned above naming 16 colleges offering an undergraduate major in physiology lists no less than 137 universities in the United States with Ph.D. programs in physiology.

The boundary line between physiology and several other biosciences is indistinct; indeed, the overlap is so great that an individual trained in one life science sometimes ends up working in another. Nobody can tell where physiology lets off and biochemistry begins, for example. Physiology also overlaps with pharmacology, anatomy, genetics, embryology, parasitology, ecology, psychology, and other disciplines. For the convenience of the author as well as that of the reader, there must be some sort of classification, so we shall proceed with a consideration of some related fields.

BIOPHYSICS

BIOPHYSICS IS ONE of the newest of the biological sciences, but it is growing rapidly. It is so closely related to physiology that in some schools biophysics and physiology are combined into one department. However, it has become sufficiently independent as a discipline for biophysicists to have organized their own society, The Biophysical Society (see Appendix).

The biophysicist's approach to biological problems utilizes the methods of modern physics, higher mathematics, and physical chemistry. The biophysicist addresses himself to some very basic issues, but his results often have practical consequences. Biophysics has contributed to the study of cancer, to the design of computers—which are analagous in some respects to the human brain—and to the development of new drugs.

All matter, living and nonliving, is made up of molecules, and the most complicated molecules in our bodies are the proteins. A protein molecule is made up of thousands of atoms, each arranged in precise order and spatial relation to each other. Most of the hormones of the body are proteins, as are the enzymes—those important "ferments" which enable our bodies to carry on complicated chemical reactions far beyond the abilities of the most brilliant chemist to duplicate in the test tube. As this is being written, announcement has just come that two teams of scientists have succeeded for the first time in synthesizing the molecule of an enzyme. The molecule they have constructed is the enzyme ribonuclease, associated with reactions involving ribonucleic acid (RNA). Among other things, RNA is directly involved in the synthesis of proteins within the cell. It is a derivative of deoxyribonucleic acid (DNA) which is credited with the conversion of messages of the units of heredity (the genes) to actual structures in the cell. The knowledge of the structure and function of RNA and DNA has been largely developed by the biophysicist.

There is great need for more knowledge along this line. So great is the challenge that revealing the structure of even a single protein is hailed as a major scientific discovery. Much publicity has attended the recent advances in prolonging people's lives by replacing failing organs with transplants of healthy ones. The avoidance of disappointment and failure in these heroic operations will come chiefly through increased knowledge of interactions among proteins. The transplants carry proteins of a foreign body into the body of the host; the details of how these two sets of proteins interact have not been fully worked out, but many of their interactions are harmful, and this fact sets severe limitations upon the use of transplants.

Other interests of biophysicists include the effects of radiation on living matter, the details of the way in which the retina of the eye converts the energy of light into a signal to the brain, the biological effects of laser beams, the design and functioning of cardiac pacemakers. These are devices which initiate heart beats in persons whose own natural pacemakers have ceased to function properly.

The student aiming for a career in biophysics will need an extraordinarily broad base in physics, chemistry, mathematics, and biology. He (or she) should study these disciplines in high school, continue them through college, and beyond college to the doctorate. Some biophysicists recommend as many as ten courses in college mathematics. The student of biophysics will become familiar with the concepts of such subjects as protein chemistry, quantum mechanics, information theory, solid state physics, and probability theory.

Biophysicists are needed in the space program. One of the newest additions to the long list of scientific periodicals is a new journal entitled *Space Life Sciences*. Not all the articles published in this journal will be biophysical, but biophysics already plays an important role in space biology and medicine. Biophysicists are also needed in the electronics industry for the applications of nuclear power, the study of chronic diseases, the development of new medicines, and, indeed, wherever the methods of physics, chemistry, and mathematics can be applied to the solution of biological problems. There is a demand therefore for biophysicists in universities for teaching and research, and in such government laboratories as the National Institutes of Health, the Atomic Energy Commission, and in space installations. Modern hospitals, private research laboratories, and drug companies employ an increasing number of those skilled in biophysics. Some military laboratories have special biophysics branches engaged in research in such areas as space, equipment design, programs connected with advanced weaponry, and so on. In short, there are many doors open to this exciting new field of science.

Biophysics is an intellectually demanding discipline and is to be undertaken only by those who are willing to work hard and who enjoy mental stimulation. It is a highly experimental field, challenging and exciting; it utilizes the most modern concepts and instruments. If you have the basic motivation for such a study, and the capacity to meet the challenge, you will find it a most rewarding discipline.

BIOCHEMISTRY

AS THE NAME implies, biochemistry is both a biological

science and a branch of chemistry. It may be taught in departments of biology, physiology, or chemistry, but many universities have independent departments of biochemistry. Biochemistry is so closely allied with physiology that it would be difficult to make a statement about the difference between them without saying something that would bring an objection from either the physiologists or the biochemists. Perhaps it is fair to say that in most cases the difference is one of emphasis. Although the physiologist may use biochemical techniques to elucidate the functioning of a tissue or an organ, the biochemist will take special pleasure in studying the chemical processes that occur in active tissues. Both physiology and biochemistry evolved from general biology, but biochemistry could not arise until the advent of organic chemistry.

Considerable progress was made in physiology during the 19th Century, but it was not until near the close of that century that chemists became aware that all organic substances contain carbon. The chemistry of carbon compounds then became organic chemistry. Biochemistry emerged as a separate discipline when some scientists combined biology and organic chemistry and began to study chemical reactions occurring in living systems. Biochemistry is hence a younger science than physiology, and in a sense may be regarded as the offspring of a marriage between physiology and chemistry. The lineage of biochemistry is apparent in the various names that are sometimes given to it: physiological chemistry, biological chemistry, and the like.

An official publication of the American Society of Biological Chemists indicates that some of the problems biochemists are interested in solving include such questions as: How do living things obtain energy from food? How do green plants convert sunlight into the foods that are the primary source of energy for all animals including man? What is the chemical basis of heredity? How do hormones work? What causes abnormalities?

What fundamental changes occur in disease? How can these changes be modified so that health can be restored? What biochemical problems are there for the higher animals? For man? It is concluded: "There is no limit to the potentialities of the chemical approach to biological problems."

Employment opportunities for biochemists are numerous and the demand is great. Many colleges and universities offer courses in biochemistry. These are often taught in departments of biology or chemistry by specially trained biochemists. Colleges of pharmacy, dentistry, medicine, veterinary medicine, and agriculture are among the professional schools which provide opportunities for teaching or research in biochemistry. In these schools, it is not only the departments of biochemistry which employ biochemists; many of them are employed by departments of physiology, pharmacology, microbiology, anatomy, medicine, and others.

Hospitals, independent research institutes, public health departments, government laboratories, such as the famed National Institutes of Health, agricultural experiment stations are among those who benefit from the special talents of biochemists. There is also a great demand for biochemists in industrial laboratories. Food processors, drug and cosmetic manufacturers, and the huge chemical and petroleum industries constitute a continuing source of employment opportunities for those interested in applied biochemistry, in basic or applied research, or in scientific administration.

While the education of the biochemist will not differ much from that of other specialists in the health sciences, a good grasp of chemistry, mathematics, and physics is of especial importance; a biochemist may major either in biology or chemistry during his undergraduate years. Usually, specialization in biochemistry is deferred until graduate school. As with most of the sciences, the biochemist will find the widest variety of opportunities available to him if he has completed his education

beyond college through the doctorate. Although most biochemists will obtain the Ph.D. degree, some of them—as well as
some physiologists and pharmacologists—will become especially
interested in their specialty after finishing medical school. Biochemists with a medical background will usually be employed
in medical schools, hospitals, and research laboratories.

PHARMACOLOGY

TO THE AVERAGE high school or college student the
word *pharmacology* probably conveys less than does the name
of any other bioscience. Even the college senior biology major
may have only a vague notion that pharmacology might be
somehow connected with pharmacy. Unlike physiology or biochemistry, pharmacology is not found in the undergraduate
liberal arts curriculum. Yet, it offers career opportunities that
can scarcely be excelled. It is a demanding science, it offers
unique points of view, and its devotees are in short supply and
great demand.

To put it as briefly as possible, pharmacology is the study of
the interactions of drugs with living systems. By "drug" we
mean any chemical substance which can be given to a human or
animal that will affect the recipient for good or ill or which
will in any way affect the life processes. The living system
might be a microscopic part of a cell, or an organ of the body,
or a whole animal or person, healthy or sick. Physiologists also
study responses of cells, organs, and organisms, biochemists
study their chemical reactions, and pathologists examine the
effects of disease. Pharmacology, then, overlaps with those disciplines and uses their techniques. No one could be a top-notch
pharmacologist without a thorough background in physiology
and biochemistry.

Physicians and pharmacists also know a great deal about

drugs, but to be a physician or a pharmacist is not necessarily to be a pharmacologist. The pharmacologist's knowledge of drugs is unique. The intimate nature of drug action as affected by size of the dose, method of administration, solubility in various body fluids, the effects of small changes in chemical structure, and the significance of physical properties as related to drug action are among the matters of concern to the pharmacologist, but outside the specific interests of physiologists or biochemists.

Pharmacology is divided into many branches as are most other life sciences. The *general pharmacologist* tries to understand the action of a drug in all parts of the body and is often searching for better and safer drugs for treating disease. *Molecular pharmacology* is more basic in its approach and seeks to discern the interaction between a molecule of a drug and a molecule within a cell of the body. A *biochemical pharmacologist* or a *biophysical pharmacologist* uses the techniques of physics and biochemistry; sometimes his primary interest will be to determine what the body does to the drug rather than what the drug does to the body. The *clinical pharmacologist* applies all the discoveries of other pharmacologists to the human patient. His important function is to determine whether a particular drug is useful, how it should be used, and what adverse effects it may have. He bridges the gap between the original discovery of a new drug and its use by a practicing physician. He must, therefore, be versed not only in physiology, biochemistry, and pharmacology but in medicine as well. He will possess the M.D. degree, sometimes a Ph.D. as well. As you may well imagine, there is a great shortage of clinical pharmacologists.

Toxicology is a branch of pharmacology specifically concerned with the adverse effects of chemical substances, ranging all the way from minor toxic effects of useful drugs to the actions of virulent poisons. No drug is 100% safe; one of the duties of the *medical toxicologist* is to determine the limits of safety of a drug. He would hope to find out enough so that we could never again have a tragic occurrence such as the armless babies who were born of mothers taking thalidomide. The *industrial toxicologist* applies his knowledge to the health of workers in industry. The *environmental toxicologist* helps to protect public health by studying the effects of water and air pollutants, industrial wastes, household chemicals, food additives, pesticides, and the many other exposures of the modern world.

Employment opportunities in pharmacology are to be found in medical, pharmacy, and veterinary schools, as well as in government laboratories, hospitals, independent research laboratories, and in industry—especially the pharmaceutical industry. New laboratories for pharmacology are being created by industry and new medical schools are opening their doors. There is a distinct shortage of pharmacologists to fill the positions created by these newly established centers.

During the undergraduate years, the education of a future pharmacologist parallels that of a physiologist or biochemist. The study of pharmacology will generally not be undertaken until enrollment in graduate school. Ph.D. programs in pharmacology are offered in nearly all medical schools, many veterinary colleges, and some pharmacy schools. In some medical schools, the student may enroll in a combined course leading to both the Ph.D. and the M.D. degrees. Jobs in pharmacology for those lacking a doctorate are generally at the level of laboratory technician. Graduate training is essential in order to acquire the depth of knowledge which will enable the individual to do his best work. In addition, the applicant will find that employers will insist upon hiring only those with doctorates for the best jobs. This is true in all the sciences—and in some nonscientific disciplines as well—and nowhere is it more true than in pharmacology.

NUTRITION

THE SCIENCE OF nutrition should not be confused with what is commonly known as home economics, although the student of home economics must learn the basic principles of nutrition. Nutrition overlaps with other biosciences, especially with physiology and biochemistry, for it is concerned with food both as a raw material and as a nutrient. The nutritionist studies the fate of foodstuffs after digestion and absorption, their relationship to the health and welfare of both the individual and society, and how they may be related to the cause, treatment, or prevention of disease. There cannot be any doubt about the importance of a knowledge of nutrition so long as we live in a world in which 80% of the total population go to bed every night with unfilled or only partially filled stomachs and do not even know what it would feel like to be satiated.

We have all heard of the catastrophic effects on populations in the past by diseases having their roots in nutritional deficiencies. For example, the huge losses of manpower from scurvy (due to lack of vitamin C) during the days of the old sailing vessels before the ships were provisioned with lemon juice. It would be incorrect to think that such deficiency diseases are a thing of the past. One of the most distressing of all diseases is called *kwashiorkor*. This is a disease caused by protein deficiency and its victims are mainly children between the ages of six months and three years. With the type of diet that prevails in much of the world, a child within that age range simply can not eat enough to fulfill his requirement for good protein nutrition. Kwashiorkor is common throughout much of Africa, most of Asia, and some parts of Latin America. In a publication of the World Health Organization, it was said, "From the public health point of view, these children are the greatest problem in the world today." Nutritional deficiencies are by no means unknown in the impoverished areas, both urban and rural, in our own country.

Many groups, such as the Food and Agricultural Organization of the United Nations, as well as individual nations, industries, and independent research organizations, are seeking ways to correct these conditions. Those with training and skill in the science of nutrition will find useful and rewarding work in these areas. Even in our own society, although we know how to prevent such diseases as scurvy, pellagra, and beri-beri, research is still under way on the nutritional aspects of hypertension, heart ailments, obesity, tooth decay, and possibly even arthritis and cancer. Some unfortunate children are born with errors in the metabolism of foodstuffs which lead to mental retardation and early death; an example of this is the disease known as phenylketonuria. Due to the efforts of the nutritionists, many of these children have been able to develop in a nearly normal fashion, and research is continuing.

Some nutritional discoveries have far-reaching effects. I can remember when a diagnosis of pernicious anemia was almost the same as a death warrant. With the discovery of vitamin B_{12}, the means for treating this disease was at hand. But B_{12} was to have even further significance in nutrition, for it proved to be a factor which increased the efficiency with which meat animals converted hay and grain into body-building animal protein.

Biological scientists specializing in nutrition find positions teaching in universities, in medical, dental, veterinary, and agricultural schools, and sometimes in high schools. They may help to train dieticians, they work with government agencies, and many are employed by international programs, including the Peace Corps, UNICEF, and others. A demand for nutritionists exists in industry, especially industrial concerns engaged in supplying dietary supplements for either human or animal use.

The educational qualifications for a successful career in nutritional science do not differ markedly from those in other biological fields. Basic courses in chemistry, including organic chemistry and biochemistry are of importance. The biology courses should include physiology and microbiology (bacteriology). As in all sciences, the individual with an advanced degree will have a distinct advantage. Nutrition offers careers for both men and women, and there are probably few sciences in which the opportunities for members of the two sexes are more nearly equal.

PATHOLOGY

PATHOLOGISTS EXAMINE THE tissues and fluids of the body, using the techniques of biology, chemistry, and physics. Plant pathologists were discussed in Chapter 4; in this section, we shall be concerned with those pathologists who examine specimens of human or animal origin. Their findings enable them to judge whether a given specimen has come from a healthy individual or if there is disease present. The nature of the disease and the effectiveness of treatment may also be revealed. Pathology, then, is a link between basic biology and medicine. Most pathologists are physicians who have specialized in this particular field. Medicine and its specialties are beyond the scope of this book, but pathology is a basic biological science as well as a medical specialty; furthermore, there is a demand for pathologists who are not physicians. In the latter category are dental and veterinary pathologists as well as a growing number in research and service jobs who have a Ph.D. degree in pathology.

In addition to these top-grade professional jobs, there is also a brisk demand for workers in pathology laboratories especially trained for the many demanding technical jobs. These laboratory technicians and medical technologists will be discussed in the next chapter.

The Intersociety Committee on Pathology Information (see Appendix) defines pathology as the science which is concerned "with the nature of disease and the changes it causes in the body." Many diseases can be identified only by laboratory means; these include diabetes and leukemia among others. In such diseases, the pathologist also supplies the means for following the responses of the patient to treatment. The pathologist who has the training and experience necessary to qualify for a special certificate from the American Board of Pathology will have charge of a laboratory containing all the instruments and complex array of apparatus to be found in the modern biological or biochemical laboratory. He will have a staff of highly skilled assistants. In most cases he will also be a teacher, aiding in the training of medical technologists, nurses, medical students, interns, and resident physicians. In addition, he may have charge of research projects.

Laboratories concerned with studies on the safety of drugs provide a large and expanding demand for those skilled in pathology. Individuals with the Ph.D. degree in pathology, or with training in veterinary pathology find ready employment in these establishments. Studies on the safety of new drugs must be conducted at length and with great skill on experimental animals before the drug can be tried on humans. After the animals have received the new drug, the fluids and tissues of their bodies must be subjected to the same tests as those made on human patients in disease. In fact, no patient ever gets quite as thorough an examination as do these animals. Tests of this nature are performed in the laboratories of drug manufacturers, and in many laboratories operated by the government, such as the National Institutes of Health and the Food and Drug Administration. In addition, many independent laboratories carry out similar studies. Several commercial pathology laboratories perform such tests for others on a contract basis. Federal laws and regulations make such studies mandatory, and the standards are becoming higher; hence, the demand for personnel is constantly on the increase.

Professional skills of a high degree are also needed at the level of laboratory technician, technologist, and other supporting staff in the pathology laboratory. These positions, too, can be highly rewarding, and they do not require the long and tedious preparation needed by the professional pathologist (see Chapter 6).

CHAPTER 6

OTHER CAREER OPPORTUNITIES
IN APPLIED BIOLOGY

AGRICULTURAL SCIENCE

IT MAY SEEM strange that agricultural science should be included in a list of the biological sciences. The term agricultural scientist as used here is a sort of catch-all title that includes any kind of biologist whose work has an application to agriculture. This includes some taxonomists, entomologists, plant or animal pathologists, plant or animal physiologists, ecologists, nutritionists, and so on. The National Research Council has estimated that agricultural scientists whose work involves the biosciences number between 50,000 and 75,000—about one out of every five or six scientists in the U.S.A.

In Chapter 3, we spoke of the founding of the land-grant colleges—the agricultural colleges and universities—as centers of education and research in applied biology. Many agricultural scientists have received their educations at such schools. The National Academy of Sciences - National Research Council, has prepared a well-illustrated brochure on careers in agricultural science; it is entitled *Threads of Life* (see Appendix). It presents several examples of the kinds of work engaging the attention of agricultural scientists. The questions which these scientists seek to solve run through the whole spectrum of biological disciplines. Sample topics for investigation include: What do viruses do inside plants? What causes changes in fish population? What influences learning and behavior in animals? What is the importance of bacteria in the stomachs of cows, deer, and other ruminants? What causes plants to flower and set seed?—and so on.

There is a large and increasing demand for teachers of biological sciences in agricultural colleges. Many of these teachers spend part of their time in research either in laboratories on campus or in experiment stations associated with the colleges. Research agencies of the federal government and state agricultural experiment stations employ many thousands of agricultural scientists. Those in charge of the various projects typically have doctoral degrees in a biological science, but there are many rewarding jobs as assistants to scientists which can be filled by those with Bachelor's or Master's degrees. The young man or woman wishing eventually to obtain a doctorate often can fill the junior positions on the staff while working on the advanced degree.

Private research foundations employ many scientists with training in applied biology, as do industries engaged in service to agriculture, food processing, forestry products, and the like. The agricultural scientist may work in the classroom, laboratory, greenhouse, testing field, in the city or on the farm, on streams or lakes, or wherever there is need for the application of the skills of the biological scientist to the solution of the problems related to the role of agriculture in supplying food, clothing, and shelter.

The courses of instruction offered by land-grant colleges to students interested in agricultural science do not differ markedly from those which other biological scientists study during their undergraduate years, except that somewhat greater emphasis may be placed upon the practical aspects of the application of biological knowledge to agriculture. This emphasis usually comes during the latter part of the college curriculum; during the first two years the student is usually expected to obtain the same sort of broad background in basic science, mathematics, languages, and humanities which any well educated person should have. Your high school guidance counselor can give you the name of the land-grant college in your state (if you do not already know it); a letter to the Dean of Agriculture in the college will bring detailed information. Or you can write to the U. S. Office of Education, Washington, D.C. 20202, or to the Committee on Educational Policy in Agriculture, National Academy of Sciences, National Research Council, 2101 Constitution Avenue, Washington, D.C. 20418. Further suggestions will be found in the Appendix to this book.

FORESTRY

LIKE AGRICULTURAL SCIENCE, forestry is a highly practical subject. A forester must have training in both the scientific and the practical aspects of the management of something over 660 million acres of land in the U. S. suitable for forest purposes. Timber is an important biological resource, and it is the forester's job to see to it that it is used and yet perpetually maintained. Like the plant pathologist, the forester is concerned with plant diseases. Like the entomologist, he must be familiar with insects and their effects. Like the ecologist, he understands the whole of the forest environment and is interested in conservation and the management of wildlife.

Much of the forester's work is out-of-doors, but there is a great deal more to it than a perpetual hunting and fishing trip. Much of the work is arduous and hazardous. As the forester gains experience and promotion he may have more administrative and less field work to do. Forestry differs from most professions discussed in this book in one important respect: a Bachelor's or Master's degree will suffice for nearly all the available jobs. The exceptions are those jobs involving forestry research and the more advanced teaching jobs in which the doctorate will be advantageous. Nearly 50 American colleges and universities offer courses in forestry, generally a four year course leading to the degree of Bachelor of Science. A list of these schools can be obtained from the Forest Service, U. S. Department of Agriculture, Washington, D.C. 20250.

Although the federal government is the largest employer of foresters, many states, cities, universities, and private corporations employ them in increasing numbers. Private employers include lumber, pulp, paper, and other manufacturers of wood products; also railroads, water companies, recreation clubs, owners of large private estates, and others. Several departments and bureaus of the federal government employ foresters, but the majority of them are in the U. S. Forest Service. The Forest Service has prepared an excellent discussion on Careers in Forestry, obtainable from the U. S. Government Printing Office, and a book in the Vocational Guidance Manuals series is devoted to *Opportunities in a Forestry Career* (see Appendix).

LABORATORY ASSISTANTS, TECHNICIANS, AND TECHNOLOGISTS

EVERY LABORATORY ENGAGED in biological research, in biological, biochemical, or medical testing of any kind, in the care of experimental animals, or in the maintenance of collections or exhibits of biological material, as well as in many types of biological production (including industrial production of vaccines, blood fractions, etc.) must have a staff of skilled workers to conduct the daily affairs of the laboratory. Some of these positions offer not only pleasant and profitable employment, but some degree of opportunity to participate in research.

From time to time throughout this book we have mentioned the importance of laboratory technicians, and we have seen that in some instances technicians have the opportunity to study for advanced degrees and eventually to become professional bioscientists of the highest rank. It should be emphasized that not all technicians entertain ambitions for such advancement, and many of them find satisfaction in a job well done in support of the laboratory's work. In this section of this chapter, we are calling attention to certain categories of technicians who are much in demand. The individuals who fill these positions are, perhaps, not full-fledged biologists in the sense that we have used that term throughout most of this book, but they must have some training in theoretical and applied biology. They are professional technologists and they serve an important function.

Large numbers of workers are employed in medical laboratories under the direction of a pathologist. They receive special training which entitles them to be members of the Registry of Medical Technologists. The Registry is recognized across the nation. It maintains a list of scholarship and loan funds available for young people interested in studying to become laboratory technologists. It also keeps a list of approved schools. The address is: Registry of Medical Technologists, 445 North Lake Shore Drive, Chicago, Ill. 60611. The Registry is officially connected with organized medicine, but there are also several independent registries.

The American Society of Clinical Pathologists (ASCP) and the American Society of Medical Technologists recognize three general levels of laboratory workers. First is the *Certified Laboratory Assistant* (CLA) who receives accreditation after one year's study beyond high school. The CLA may obtain employment in a clinic, physician's office, public health agency,

or a variety of industrial, pharmaceutical, and military laboratories. The ASCP estimates that about 100,000 CLA's will be
needed by 1975. A second category is the *Cytotechnologist*. This
is a restricted specialty, involving microscopic study of cells to
assist in the diagnosis of cancer. This specialty requires two
years of college, with an emphasis on biology, and an additional
year at a school of cytotechnology. More than 100 such schools
have been approved by the American Medical Association, and
it is estimated that 1,000 newly trained cytotechnologists are
needed annually. Generous scholarships for students in cytotechnology are available from the American Cancer Society and
the Cancer Control Program of the U. S. Public Health Service.
Information regarding these scholarships can be obtained from
the Intersociety for Research Potential in Pathology (see Appendix).

To be a *medical technologist* requires four years of study
beyond high school: three years in college with courses in
biology, chemistry, and mathematics, and a fourth year in an
accredited technology school studying under the direction of a
pathologist. Many universities give a combined course, so the
whole four years may be obtained in one location. A Bachelor's
degree is awarded at the end of the course of study. There are
nearly 800 schools fully accredited in medical technology, but
they cannot keep up with the demand. The Registry of Medical
Technologists recently estimated that some 90,000 professional
medical technologists will be needed within the next decade.
About 50,000 are currently registered, but only about 37,000 of
them are currently working—the rest have either retired, or
have quit work temporarily because of family responsibilities.
The medical technologist has an interesting variety of work to
do, performing chemical, microscopic, bacteriological, and other
tests. They work in laboratories connected with physician's
offices, hospitals and clinics, independent service laboratories,
university laboratories, government agencies, and industry.

Technologists often advance to become supervisors, teachers, or research assistants.

Other technologists recognized and registered by the official Registry include the *histologic technician,* who prepares microscope slides of sections of tissues so they can be studied by the pathologist—one year of training beyond high school makes one eligible for this specialty; the *microbiology technologist* must have a Bachelor's degree, preferably with a microbiology major, followed by a year's experience beyond college. The *blood bank technologist* also requires a baccalaureate degree, with a major in biology, followed by a year in a school approved by the American Association of Blood Banks.

BIOLOGICAL WRITING AS A CAREER

MOST SCIENTISTS DO some writing as part of their careers. The educator may write reports on new teaching techniques he has tried, or on especially informative experiences in the classroom. The field worker often makes observations which need to be communicated to his colleagues. The research worker, especially in a college or university, must write papers reporting the results of his research; unless he does so, his research has not really contributed anything to knowledge, nor is he so likely to receive rapid promotion in his job, no matter how skillful he may be in other aspects of his work. The amount of such writing is enormous; the National Library of Medicine in Washington, D.C., acquires more than 90,000 research papers each year.

The scientist who has written a number of such reports will sometimes undertake a more ambitious writing project in the form of an advanced treatise or "monograph." A monograph is a highly specialized book attempting to cover what is known about a specific—and usually rather narrowly circumscribed—

aspect of a subject. A monograph may have a single author, or different authors may write the various chapters in the book, with one of them serving as editor of the entire monograph. Topics available for subjects of biological monographs are endless. For example, a single recent issue of *American Scientist* contained book reviews of about a dozen such monographs, bearing such titles as *Hummingbirds and Their Flowers, Viruses in Plant Hosts, The Natural History and Behavior of the California Sea Lion, Nematode Parasites of Domestic Animals and of Man.*

Other kinds of books written by professional biologists include laboratory handbooks and textbooks intended for class use. The number of scientific books is constantly growing. Most publishers send each of their new books to the editors of *American Scientist* in the hope that they will receive favorable reviews. The number of such new books received for review each year exceeds a thousand, and the editors of *American Scientist* engage more than 350 scientists to read and review the books received.

In a somewhat different category is writing done for the general reader. This may take the form of articles for news-papers or magazines, columns reporting the latest developments, interpreting science news for the public, or answering readers' questions. Popular nontechnical books addressed to the general reader are also in demand.

In the past, scientists in general and biologists in particular have been highly critical of much of the reporting of science news in papers and magazines. Many of the reporters lacked scientific insight and thought in terms of the "human interest" of their stories. This handicap, coupled with the lack of coopera-tion from biologists who often held themselves to be "above" talking to representatives of the press, sometimes led to mis-leading stories. Mistakes still occur in some science reporting, but in general there has been a trend for the press to hire science reporters who have had training in biology—some of them even hold advanced degrees. Such people are truly professional science writers, and they have formed an organization to improve standards. With this change in reporting has also come a change in the average biologist's attitude toward the press; many meetings of biologists now feature newsrooms where scientists and reporters can meet together, and some biological societies prepare news releases describing in a non-technical fashion some of the reports presented by the scientists to their assembled colleagues.

Generally speaking, the biologist who writes the kinds of papers mentioned in the first paragraph of this section will receive no monetary compensation for his efforts. Technical journals appeal only to a limited readership and can not afford to pay their authors; indeed, sometimes the author's institution is required to pay "page charges" to the journal! The author of an advanced technical manual or monograph fares somewhat better—but not much. These highly specialized books cost just as much to produce as does a basic textbook and sometimes more. A leading publisher of scientific books has recently revealed that the average sale of a monograph is on the order of 4,000 copies. It is easy to see that the cost per copy of such a book will be far greater than that of a textbook which may sell 100,000 copies. So not only does the monograph have a limited appeal but its high price further reduces its sales. Hence, no matter how favorable the author's royalty agreement may be, the scientist should not consider writing a book about his specialty as a means of supplementing his income. His rewards must be the more intangible ones of prestige and the personal satisfactions that come from a job well done and from seeing one's name in print.

Either popular writing or textbook writing, on the other hand, can be profitable either as a sideline or in some instances as a full time career. Beginning authors sometimes have illusions about their writing abilities, the importance of their manuscripts, and the financial returns to be expected. Skill in writing sufficient to turn out acceptable manuscripts requires years of practice beyond what can be learned in a freshman composition course. Although publishers will read unsolicited manuscripts, the most favorable reception will likely be given to manuscripts which the editor is expecting. The groundwork may be laid by previous correspondence between editor and author, but authors who are interested in writing as a full time career usually employ literary agents.

Even the most popular books on biological subjects seldom reach the bestseller category, and the most successful authors of textbooks and books for the general reader generally have several books on the market at the same time. In that way, royalties will be coming in from older books while the newer ones are establishing their places in the market. A few individuals have built rewarding careers in this way. One successful author, Herbert S. Zim, has written an article on "Writing Careers in Biology" which was published in the April, 1968, issue of *The American Biology Teacher,* the official publication of the National Association of Biology Teachers. If you wish to read further about biological writing as a career, from the point of view of a successful professional, try to obtain a copy of that article.

CHAPTER 7

THE EMPLOYERS OF BIOLOGISTS

FROM TIME TO time in previous chapters, we have made brief mention of some of the places where biologists work—the organizations, institutions, and industries which employ them. We can now summarize some of this information and add some further details.

EDUCATIONAL INSTITUTIONS

PEOPLE WITH BIOLOGICAL training find employment in nearly every kind of secondary and higher educational establishment. The greatest numbers are those teaching biology in secondary schools, including both public high school schools and private schools. No exact figure is available, but they seem to number about 30,000 or more. There are not enough to meet the demand. Not all high school biology teachers are primarily biologists; many of them teach other subjects, usually other sciences; in the smaller schools teachers do not necessarily specialize in one subject or in a few related subjects. As employers, high schools generally use different criteria in hiring

116

than do other employers of biologists. The high school teacher will usually be required to have studied courses in teaching methods and in science education in addition to biology and related sciences. The beginning teacher will be expected to have a Bachelor's degree, or preferably a Master's degree. In addition, he may be expected to continue his education by summer study or other means.

Colleges and universites are not far behind secondary schools in their demands for teachers of biological subjects. There are probably about 25,000 such teachers, with the number increasing at the rate of about 1,000 each year. Unlike the secondary school teacher, the university teacher of biology is likely to consider himself as *primarily* a professional biologist. College teachers usually earn a doctorate degree before obtaining a position as a full-time faculty member, although some of the smaller colleges may hire a candidate who will complete his study for the advanced degree during the early years of his teaching career. The advanced degree, Ph.D. or Sc.D., is awarded as a result of concentrated study of a highly specialized field, and colleges will consider for hiring only those indivduals whose specialized study is closely related to the subject which the new instructor is expected to teach. If you obtain a Ph.D. in a Department of Education, for example, you cannot expect to obtain a job teaching in a Department of Biology.

The preparation for a teaching career in a college is the same as that for a full-time research worker (see Chapter 3). Most colleges and universities, especially the larger ones and those with the greatest prestige, expect faculty members to combine teaching and research careers. In that way, the college teacher not only passes along to the next generation the knowledge accumulated in the past, but also keeps in the forefront of new developments. The young man or woman just beginning a teaching career in college will usually be given the title of instructor. As he becomes more experienced he rises to assistant professor, then associate professor, and finally professor. With each increase in rank there is an improvement in salary, greater opportunities to teach more advanced courses and guide young graduate students who will be the next generation of college teachers, and greater responsibilities in serving on committees which help guide the policies of the institution.

Colleges offer many attractions for those considering a teaching career. They are frequently located in pleasant towns or in cities with many cultural advantages. The faculty members form a community of people with a similar level of education, and with many interests, hopes, and aspirations in common. To an extraordinary degree, the teacher is his own boss, free to plan his own time and to do his work in his own way. There will be more to say along this line in the next chapter on rewards of a biological career.

Many universities have more than one department which employ biological scientists while smaller colleges may have but a single department of biology. Larger ones may have seperate departments of botany and zoology. Many other arrangements are possible, and there may be several departments representing the various biological disciplines. Colleges of agriculture, with their emphasis on applied biology, utilize an especially large variety of biological skills. Specialists in several biosciences are to be found in colleges of medicine, dentistry, pharmacy, and veterinary medicine; these schools are usually integral parts of universities, but some are independent.

It might be helpful for you to visit one or more of the colleges or professional schools near you, seek out the biologists working in them, and talk with them. The more different kinds of biologists you talk with, the better your own judgment may be about selecting a similar kind of career. You will find most of them glad for a chance to talk about their work, and especially happy to welcome a prospective recruit to their profession.

But don't expect them to make up your mind for you; you must do that yourself.

If you are considering biology teaching for a career, you should not overlook the possibilities offered by the junior college or community college. Although the courses of instruction are not as advanced as one can find in four-year colleges, most of them offer courses of sufficient diversity to interest most biologists. In some instances, their programs of general biology are at least as good as those of the lower divisions of four-year colleges. The ability and motivation of the students in these institutions are varied; they range all the way from college "under-achievers" and "late bloomers" to highly enthusiastic adults. Unlike the four-year college, the junior college often requires applicants for teaching jobs to obtain teaching certificates.

Requirements for certification of junior college teachers differ from state to state. For specific information, you may contact the department of education of your state university. A general summary of requirements for junior college teachers is to be found in "A Survey of Junior College Certification Requirements in the United States," by Bruce W. Burkhart, a biology teacher in Rio Hondo Junior College, Whittier, California.*

The teaching load—that is, the actual number of hours per week actually spent in the classroom—is usually somewhat less than that required in high school, but greater than that demanded in the senior college. Often, salary scales are lower in junior college than in either high school or four-year college, but they are rapidly improving. If a teacher wishes to spend part of his time in research, he will find that the junior college offers less opportunity than does the senior college. There are, then, some frustrations accompanying junior college teaching, but the dedicated and enthusiastic teacher finds that they add to

---

* In *The American Biology Teacher,* November, 1967, vol. 29, p. 8.

the interest and challenge of the job. Bruce W. Burkhart has summed up this point of view as follows: "I am convinced that the junior college offers the most exciting and professionally rewarding field in higher education."**

GOVERNMENTAL AGENCIES

THE LARGEST EMPLOYER of biologists or of those whose work is closely related to biology is the federal government. Biologists may be found in most of the departments. Let us look, for example, at the Department of Interior which is charged with the duty of conservation of natural resources. A list of the agencies within that department which employ bioscientists and biologically oriented people would have to include the Bureau of Commercial Fisheries, Bureau of Sport Fisheries and Wildlife, Bureau of Land Management, National Park Service, Bureau of Outdoor Recreation, Geological Survey, Federal Water Pollution Control Administration, Bureau of Reclamation, Office of Saline Water, Office of Water Resources Research, Bureau of Indian Affairs, Office of Territories, and Office of the Science Advisor. But for all that, the Department of the Interior is overshadowed by the Department of Agriculture, which is the largest employer of biologists.

The multiplicity of jobs within the federal government is indicated by the following list—a very incomplete list—issued by various agencies and classified in biological sciences:

Agricultural Bacteriologist	Biological Aide
Agricultural Technology	Cereal Technologist
Agricultural Extension	Cotton Technologist
Agronomy	Dairy Husbandman
Animal Physiology	Ecologist
Bacteriology	Editor
Biology	Entomology

** In *The American Biology Teacher,* April, 1968, vol. 30, p. 274.

Fish Culture
Fishery Research Biology
Forestry
Forestry Aide
Forestry Research
Gardening
Genetics
Herbarium Aide
Horticulture
Hydrologist
Illustrator
Investigator
Librarian
Medical Biology Technician
Microbiology
Microanalysis
Mycology
Nematology
Nutritionist
Parasitology
Park Naturalist
Park Ranger
Pharmacology
Plant Pathology
Plant Physiology
Plant Taxonomy
Poultry Husbandman
Predator and Rodent Control
Range Management and Conservation
Seed Technology
Soil Science
Systematic Zoology
Tree Culture
Wildlife Management
Wildlife Research Biology
Zoology

The above list of 50 jobs in various government agencies is a purely arbitrary one of actual titles of positions selected by the author and arranged alphabetically. You can judge its incompleteness by the fact that the Department of Agriculture alone has a list more than twice as long. Some of the categories, though, seem to be less directly related to biology than are those above.

A career in government service has many attractive features for biologists. Employment conditions for all scientists in the government have been vastly improved within the past decade or so, and biologists in particular have benefited from increasing emphasis on life sciences which had previously been somewhat neglected in favor of the physical sciences. Applicants for positions related to biological science do not need to take a civil service examination; they are hired on the basis of education and experience. The levels of jobs range all the way from the so-called "blue collar" jobs for those who have not completed college to the so-called "supergrades"—GS-16, 17, and 18—with distinguished scientists receiving salaries of more than $20,000 annually.

For those who start to work before completing their training, the government offers training programs. Arrangements are made for the employee to receive full pay while attending classes at a nearby university part time, or even full time up to one year. After completing this training, of course, the employee is in line for a job with a higher rating.

Government positions offer an unusual degree of security. The security is protected by the civil service system, and there is little danger that the employee will lose his job as long as he wants to keep it. The salary scale is nearly as good as that in private industry, and somewhat better than in the educational world. The government scientist has good laboratories and equipment available to him, and much freedom in doing the job in his own way. He can publish the results of his work in the scientific journals, and hence achieve a reputation in the world of science; he can attend scientific meetings with part or all of the expenses paid. The fringe benefits of group life insurance, health insurance, and retirement pay are comparable to those received by scientists working in private industry, except that companies usually pay more of the cost than does the government. A scientist who works in the laboratory or in the field may wish to continue to do so for his entire career or he may choose to become an executive and help to administer the programs of his department. Either way, there are plenty of opportunities for advancement.

Although the government service is centered around Washington, D.C., employees of such agencies as the Department of Agriculture, the Department of the Interior, the Public Health Service, and others are to be found in all the states and in some instances their duties take them overseas.

We should not leave the area of federal service without mentioning the Food and Drug Administration. This important agency, a part of the Department of Health, Education, and Welfare, employs a large number of biological scientists and has a continuing need for biologists, chemists, and other scientists of the highest caliber. The FDA is charged with the duty of ensuring that foods, drugs, and cosmetics sold in the United States are safe, properly manufactured, honestly advertised, and effective for the purpose for which they are sold (some foods, especially meats, are inspected by the Department of Agriculture).

Each of the states, and some cities, employ biological scientists in roles similar to many of the federal jobs. Biologically oriented agencies of state and local governments include fish and game commissions, parks, aquariums, arboretums, museums, and the like. On the average, these positions pay slightly less than comparable jobs in the federal service, and such fringe benefits as vacation time, sick leave, insurance, and retirement pay are not quite as generous as those enjoyed by federal workers.

In summary, whatever your interests in biology might be—whether you would like to work outdoors in field or forest, streams or seas, or indoors in laboratory or at a desk, in routine work or in research, in doing your own work or in supervising and administering the work of others—a place can be found in government service. If, however, you want to experience the thrill of bringing young people into their first contact with the exciting world of biology, and watch them mature into scientists in their own right, you will do better in teaching.

INDUSTRY

ACCORDING TO A report of a committee of the 88th Congress, industry performs 75% of all research and development in our country. Individuals with biological qualifications are employed by an astonishing variety of business and industrial concerns. An indication of the importance of this source of employment for biologists can be obtained by listing some of the industries involved. The chemical industry offers many opportunities. Prominent in this category are those firms producing agricultural chemicals, including substances used for controlling pests or stimulating crop production, as well as dietary supplements for nutrition of animals or humans.

Among those offering positions with biological orientation are processors of foods and beverages, the manufacturers of cosmetics, the agricultural industries needing the skills of animal husbandmen or plant husbandmen, the breeders of fur-bearing animals, fisheries, forest products companies, and even such concerns as the manufacturers of textiles, leather goods, and petroleum products, as well as public utility companies and the aerospace industry. Still others are the publishers of biological books, manufacturers of laboratory equipment, general laboratory supply houses, and those companies which make a business of collecting, culturing, and processing biological material for the use of educational institutions and research laboratories. There is scarcely any biological discipline mentioned in this book that is not represented in one or more of the industries just listed.

One growing industry is made up of companies which perform scientific services under contract for others. Some of them do biological testing exclusively, while others include biology but have other departments as well. The customers of the biological testing companies include the U. S. government, drug companies, cosmetic manufacturers, and a variety of other individuals and corporations. Many of the customers have testing laboratories of their own but sometimes need the additional help of the service companies. Although much of the work is routine, the testing laboratories also do a considerable amount of research and some of their bioscientists are highly regarded by their colleagues in other organizations. The biological disciplines represented in this industry include nutrition, biochemistry, physiology, pharmacology, microbiology, cytology, histology, toxicology, and pathology.

The demand for the services of the testing laboratories is so great that new companies are organized from time to time and the old ones are expanding, so that there is a continuing demand for biologically oriented personnel at all levels from laboratory assistant to research scientist. A few of the better known laboratories of this kind are: Arthur D. Little, Inc., Cambridge, Mass.; Food and Drug Research Laboratories, Inc., New York, N.Y.; Hazleton Laboratories, Falls Church, Va.; Industrial Biotest Laboratories, Chicago, Ill.; International Research and Development Corp., Mattawan, Mich.—there are many others.

The drug manufacturers probably employ more biologists than any other industry. The research laboratories of the drug industry employ about 20,000 people, of whom nearly 4,000 hold Ph.D. degrees. The industry spends the extraordinarily high figure of 11.4% of its sales revenue on research and development. The company with the largest budget for research—Merck—allotted $61 million for that purpose in 1969. For our present discussion, the significance of such figures is that the scientist in the pharmaceutical industry is, by and large, given whatever he needs in the way of materials, equipment, and assistants to do the job he needs to do. The work is expensive, partly because of some 175,000 new chemicals tested in a year, not more than 8 out of each 1,000 show enough promise to warrant testing in humans, and most of those are rejected before marketing.

In spite of these difficulties, the industry points with pride to a report by the U. S. Department of Health, Education, and Welfare showing that research by American drug companies over a period of 28 years produced 457 of the 525 major drugs that were discovered, developed, and approved for marketing. The importance of some of these drugs may be illustrated by the fact that in 1968 there were 291,000 *fewer* people in mental hospitals than there would have been if the pattern of admissions had continued the same as it was before the discovery of the drugs for treating mental illness.*

The research biologist in the drug industry is able, to a degree unmatched anywhere else, to work in collaboration with scientists in disciplines other than his own, whether physical sciences or other biosciences. Cooperation between biologists and chemists is a daily occurrence, and the biologist often consults with physicists, mathematicians, psychologists, and pharmacists, to mention a few. Bioscience disciplines represented in the industry include physiology, biochemistry, toxicology, pharmacology, pathology, animal husbandry, microbiology, immunology, systematic botany, entomology, and nutrition.

Papers and monographs written by industrial scientists are published in the leading scientific journals and books, and research workers in industry often hold high positions in scientific societies. These are developments of the past few years, for many of us can remember when scientists who worked for industry—especially biological scientists—were held in low esteem by their academic colleagues. A major reason for improvement in this attitude is the enlightened attitude of many companies who have come to realize that scientists require a different kind of environment than do people with commercial interests. Now, there is a fair amount of interchange between the academic world and industry; some university professors forsake academia for jobs in industry, while many scientists leave industry for teaching positions. In addition, many industrial scientists hold part-time teaching appointments in nearby universities.

The professional levels of biologists in the drug industry range all the way from beginners with baccalaureate degrees

---

* According to figures published in *Today's Health,* October, 1968.

working as technicians to scientists of international renown. The beginner is encouraged to continue his education while receiving full pay from the company; most companies pay the tuition charges for part-time study at a nearby college or university. Many of the pharmaceutical laboratories are built in pleasant rural or suburban locations, in keeping with efforts to make working conditions as pleasant as possible. Salaries are slightly higher than in colleges, and the fringe benefits of vacations, sick leave, insurance, pensions, etc. are among the most liberal of any industry.

Jobs with biological orientation are becoming more common in industry, in addition to the positions in research departments. Some companies prefer professionally trained representatives to present their products to customers. These are not salesmen in the old sense but individuals who provide a liaison between company and customer. Others employ professional people in training programs for sales personnel and technical representatives. If you can combine technical competence with a flair for writing you will find that there is a brisk demand for staff writers and editors. In summary, despite obvious differences between the academic life and industry, you will find the same types of people in both, and there are as many varieties of opportunities in one as in the other.

SELF-EMPLOYMENT OPPORTUNITIES

ONE OTHER COMMERCIAL outlet for biological talent remains to be discussed: namely, the biologist who goes into business for himself. We have already discussed the biological testing industry; several of the laboratories in that category were started by biological scientists. Starting such a project requires an amount of capital that is not readily available to everyone. Easier to start are laboratories which perform testing services for physicians and hospitals. Although most hospitals have their own laboratories for biological and biochemical examinations, there are also large numbers of independent laboratories performing such services. To be successful in such a venture, you should have a thorough background in the technical aspects of biochemistry, hematology, and in the preparation of microscope slides. The more successful of such ventures have proven to be highly rewarding financially.

Self-employment opportunities are also available for botanists. Some of them become greenhouse operators who may engage in a particularly lucrative specialty, such as the growing of orchids. Botanical systematists become consultants to industry. Plant pathologists are also in demand as consultants and some of them go into private practice. The number of self-employed botanists is small but some find that their business pays well.

The collection, preservation, and sale of biological specimens is another source of self-employment. Vast numbers of living and preserved frogs, turtles, earthworms, sharks, sea urchins, anemones, seaweeds, and other organisms both plant and animal are used for teaching and research in schools, colleges, and research laboratories. The demand for them is constantly growing as the number of students of biology increases and schools become more generous in their budgetary allowances for materials.

There are many companies that seek to fill this demand and most of them were started by individuals who turned their knowledge and enthusiasm for biological collecting into a profitable business. Just to give two examples: the firm of J. R. Schettle Biologicals, Stillwater, Minn., was founded about 50 years ago by the father of the present owner and has grown to the point where 60 acres are required just to provide the ponds, streams, and woodland required to hold their specimens until they are sold. A firm specializing in marine fauna, the

Gulf Specimen Co., Panacea, Fla., though founded as recently as 1962 has grown to the point where three collecting boats are kept busy. The founder, Jack Rudloe, who now gives employment to other collectors, has expressed his enthusiasm not only in building up a lucrative business but by writing about his specialty. If you are interested, you may wish to read "Science in Action—The Biological Collector" in *Natural History Magazine,* November, 1964, vol. 73, p. 59, or the book *The Sea Brings Forth* by Jack Rudloe, published by Alfred A. Knopf, Inc., New York, in 1968.

INDEPENDENT RESEARCH LABORATORIES

RESEARCH LABORATORIES WHICH are neither directly connected with industry nor a part of a specific department of a university receive their support in a variety of ways. Some of them depend largely upon the income from endowment funds which have been donated by an individual or group wishing to use their wealth in a constructive way. Others depend more upon annual contributions. Most of them accept grants of money from government funds or from interested industries. Whatever their sources of income, large numbers of bioscientists ranging in rank and status all the way from laboratory assistants to Nobel Prize winning scientists find a stable and congenial atmosphere for their research. The same wide range of biological and biomedical disciplines are to be found in the independent research laboratories as in universities or industrial installations. The qualifications for appointment are the same, and salaries and fringe benefits do not differ greatly. In some of them, it is also possible to participate in the education and training of young scientists and to hold faculty rank in a nearby university.

Here are just a few examples of the independent laboratories: the Marine Biological Laboratory, Woods Hole, Massachusetts, is a favorite spot for many biologists—especially marine biologists—in the summer time, but research activity goes on the year around; the laboratory also maintains active collecting and culturing activities. The Research Triangle Park in North Carolina, a joint venture of three universities, is not simply a laboratory but a collection of laboratories including biological and other sciences. The Worcester Foundation for Experimental Biology, Shrewsbury, Mass., is famed for its work on endocrine physiology (especially for its origin of "The Pill") but carries on other biological work, too. The Salk Institute of Biological Studies in San Diego is named in honor of its Director, Dr. Jonas Salk of polio vaccine fame. There are independent laboratories in every section of the country.

BOTANICAL GARDENS AND ARBORETUMS

IF YOU HAVE never visited a botanical garden or arboretum, it may surprise you to learn that there are many kinds of careers available in these interesting places and a considerable demand for men and women to fill staff positions. Botanical gardens are more than just beautiful displays of trees and flowers. They typically have many varieties of plants growing in the open, and more in greenhouses and conservatories. The care of these plants is much more demanding than that of the usual commercial greenhouse or nursery. The latter will have no more than a few dozen kinds of plants, but a large botanical garden may have several thousand different species of plants, each with its own particular requirements for growth and propagation. In addition, botanical gardens and arboretums maintain collections of dried specimens. These collections can be very large—the New York Botanical Garden has more than three million specimens.

These gardens are not merely repositories of stationary specimens. They are also educational institutions and many of them also conduct extensive research. Some of the subjects of research are ecology, plant anatomy, systematic botany, economic botany, plant physiology, phytopathology, biochemistry, and a host of other topics. Sometimes, research botanists and curators hold professorships in nearby universities. Graduate students in some departments of botany can complete all their research for advanced degrees at a botanical garden or arboretum.

There is an urgent demand for staff members with training and skills required for participation in the educational programs which botanical gardens offer to school children and to the general public. These programs consist not only of labeled collections of living plants, but also of exhibits, classes, lectures, publications, and the furnishing of background material in botany for schools of all levels. Dr. William Steere, Director of the New York Botanical Garden, has stated it this way: "specialized staff members to schedule school visits, interact with teachers, and bring some impact on school curricula, are desperately needed."

The kinds of jobs available in botanical gardens and arboretums include gardeners, horticulturists, caretakers for the herbarium, staff members for preparing exhibits, directors of educational activities, editors and writers for the publication programs, librarians, research scientists, and many others. In some instances there are opportunities for travel to remote parts of the globe for the systematic exploration and collection of new (or old) plants. This may serve many purposes, such as adding to the collections, improving the exhibits, aiding in the preservation of plant species threatened with extinction, and discovering new species of value as ornamentals or as food plants or as sources of new drugs.

If you wish to consider a career in this field, you should visit at least one botanical garden or arboretum, and preferably more than one, since they differ markedly in size, organization, and activities. Make an appointment with the director or other staff member, discuss your interests with him, and observe the place in action. If you don't know where there is such a garden near you, consult the volume *The Arboretums and Botanical Gardens of North America* by Donald Wyman, published by the Arnold Arboretum of Harvard University.

ZOOS

WHAT THE BOTANICAL gardens do for plants, zoos do for animals. In addition, since animals have such fascination for people of all ages, attendance at zoos exceeds that at botanical gardens. In fact, no professional sport draws as many spectators as do the zoos. Zoos provide public recreation and outdoor amusement, but more importantly they are educational and research institutions. The educational activities of zoos include informative exhibits for the general public, the publication of guide books, tours for school children, orientation programs for school teachers—sometimes courses are given in cooperation with local colleges so that teachers may earn credit—public lectures and films, television programs, and facilities for the use of advanced students for the study of animal behavior. There are sometimes special programs for particular groups, such as clubs interested in birds or some other animal group, Boy or Girl Scouts, photographers, artists, or others.

The importance of these activities varies with the size and resources of the zoo. They are carried on not only at the zoo, but there may be classroom follow-ups with zoological specimens taken to schools. The zoo employees most often encountered by the public are the groundsmen, keepers, and their assistants. Keepers are practical animal husbandmen; recently, there has been a tendency to elevate the positions professionally and to demand more training than in the past. Curators are the professional zoologists in the zoo, and positions as curators are often held by individuals with Master's or Ph.D. degrees. Curators not only supervise the care of the animals, but make decisions on the choice of animals to display and the means used to present the displays to the public.

The zoologist in the zoo may perform research on animal breeding, genetics, ecology, animal behavior, or other topics. He may need to travel to visit other zoos, or to study animals in their native state, or to collect specimens. Although the most familiar animals in the zoo may be the mammals, there must also be experts on birds (ornithologists), reptiles and amphibians (herpetologists), and fish (ichthyologists). An aquarium for the study and display of fish and other aquatic creatures is often associated with a zoo, but it may be separate. Workers at zoos and aquariums find that their work never gets dull, they are relatively free from bureaucratic regulations, and their salaries are comparable with those of people of corresponding education and responsibility in local schools and colleges.

MUSEUMS OF NATURAL HISTORY

MOST OF US like to make collections of interesting objects, and the greatest collections of objects of scientific interest are in natural history museums. Museums play an important role in transmitting scientific information to the public, hence they are of increasing significance as informal educational institutions. The most visible evidence of the museum's educational function is the exhibit. Museum exhibition as a profession has a strong appeal to certain persons, but the employment opportunities are limited. Often, exhibits are prepared by staff members whose primary duties lie elsewhere, but there is an increasing tendency for museum exhibition to become a profession in its own right.

Exhibits are educational displays. Their preparation involves conception and planning followed by design and execution. The exhibitor, then, is less of a specialist than are most biologists. Not only must he be well grounded in general biology, but he should especially understand systematics, ecology, and conservation. In addition, he should know something about the principles of three-dimensional design, color harmony, photography, and the like. He will have some contact with anthropology, paleontology, geology, and geography—he does not need to be an "expert" in these fields, but should have sufficient understanding of them to be able to collaborate with professionals in such disciplines. Dr. A. G. Wright, of the Museum of Natural History, Smithsonian Institution, has put it this way: "The professional practitioner of museum exhibition, as here envisaged, might be more accurately described as a generalist."*

The exhibit is by no means the only educational medium of the natural history museum. Many museums contain classrooms, and museum personnel often collaborate with local school systems in informal instruction either in the museum or in the schools. The museum's collections are also important sources of material for instructional purposes or for scholarly research. The curator in a large natural history museum is generally a systematic biologist (see Chapter 4). The duties of the curator are manifold: he occasionally makes field trips to remote areas for specimens. Once the specimen is in the museum's collection, it has to be properly identified, documented, labeled, and maintained in condition for proper use by scholars not only now but in future generations. The curator also helps in the exhibit programs, collaborates with his colleagues in other institutions, gives lectures—both technical and popular—and he must do scholarly research in his field and publish the results in technical journals. In many instances, he holds an appointment on a university faculty (some important museums are integral parts of universities) and aids in the instruction of advanced students, especially graduate students.

---

*"Museum Exhibition: A Reappraisal", A. G. Wright, *The American Biology Teacher*, April, 1968, vol. 30, p. 302.

A limited number of positions are available as assistants in natural history museums. In general, these positions are filled by applicants who have Bachelor's degrees with majors in biology. In former years, many museum assistants were eventually promoted to curatorial positions, even without additional formal education. With the increasing emphasis upon research in systematic biology, appointment or promotion to the title of Curator today goes only to those who have completed the training for the Ph.D. degree. Many museums have training programs for technicians, and the technical assistant may be able to obtain the formal education necessary for promotion.

The jobs available in museums do not compare in numbers with those in teaching or in industry or in government research, but for the limited number who find employment in them, museums offer an enjoyable environment. There are few careers that instill greater dedication on the part of their devotees. If you are interested in pursuing further the possibilities of a career in museum work, you should make an appointment with a curator in a museum near your home, or write to the American Association of Museums, 2306 Massachusetts Ave., N.W., Washington, D.C. 20008.

THE PEACE CORPS

WE SHOULD NOT leave the subject of nonprofit employers of biologists without mentioning the Peace Corps. This organization, established by President Kennedy in 1961, consists of volunteers who serve for some two years in an underdeveloped country which has invited the Peace Corps to send people for specific kinds of service in their country. The purposes of the Corps are to help interested countries to meet their needs for trained manpower, to promote better understanding of Americans on the part of the peoples served, and better understanding of other peoples by Americans. Peace Corps volunteers receive no salary, but transportation and health needs are cared for, and monthly allowances are sufficient to cover modest living costs. An additional allowance is given upon return to the United States to permit readjustment to life in this country.

Biologically trained Peace Corps volunteers are serving in many areas of the globe. Most of them are either teaching in secondary schools or teacher training schools or assisting in field work. Among the requests that host countries have made, the following may be listed as of interest to biologists:

> Training teachers in general biology, botany, bacteriology.
> Teaching biology in secondary school and in teachers' training colleges.
> Teaching in agricultural school.
> Training agricultural extension personnel.
> Medical technologists to train hospital technicians.
> Aiding in malaria control and in training others for malaria control.
> Supervising operations and training in forestry.
> Volunteers for help in fresh water fisheries, in fish farming, in wildlife management, in conservation.
> Volunteers trained in marine biology, in limnology, in ecology.

The above tabulation was selected from a list published by the Peace Corps in a single year; in another year, there might be additional requests. The Peace Corps would seldom if ever become a permanent occupation, but among the services offered by the Corps to returning volunteers is career information, advice, and counseling for readjustment to life in this country.

The Corps operates an active recruiting program with recruiters visiting campuses. It also publishes a number of booklets describing the operations and the opportunities for service. Incidentally, although the majority of volunteers are young people, the Corps accepts volunteers of all ages, including retirees. Peace Corps offices are maintained in various regions of the country, or you may obtain full information by writing to: Peace Corps, Washington, D.C. 20525.

CHAPTER 8

GETTING STARTED

AT THIS STAGE, when you are considering biology as a career but probably haven't fully decided upon it, it is too early to be overly concerned about the means of obtaining employment, but perhaps a brief summary of how biologists obtain jobs will not be out of place. There are, of course, employment agencies, including teachers agencies. They maintain files of jobs available and of candidates for jobs. They are in the job-finding business for profit, and you may have to pay a modest registration fee to have your name listed; in addition, the agency collects some agreed upon portion of the first year's salary.

COLLEGE PLACEMENT BUREAUS

MANY COLLEGES HAVE placement bureaus which aid their graduates in finding jobs during the early stages of their careers. These may be especially useful in finding teaching jobs. Companies often send recruiters to campuses for employment interviews, especially companies looking for graduate students about to complete their requirements for the Ph.D. degree. This kind of recruitment, however, is more commonly done in the physical sciences than in biological sciences. Companies with vacancies in their research labs will sometimes ask a likely candidate to visit them; all expenses will be paid, and the candidate wined and dined and given the red-carpet treatment. Don't expect this as a beginner; such treatment is reserved for someone who has already established a reputation in his field and who has some talent the company is looking for. Even a beginner, though, can have an interview if he will write either to the director of the laboratory where he wishes to apply or to the personnel department of the company.

PROFESSIONAL JOURNALS

A FEW PROFESSIONAL and scientific journals have classified advertising sections with advertisements for "Positions Wanted" and "Positions Open." *Science, BioScience,* and the *Bulletin of the American Association of University Professors* are examples of such journals. The classified sections of the Sunday edition of large metropolitan newspapers—especially The New York *Times*—also carry employment advertisements in biological sciences. As this is being written, I have on my desk several recent issues of *Science* and *BioScience.* The "Positions Open" columns include calls for the following kinds of biologists, among others: general biologist, aquatic biologist interested in taxonomy, entomologist (for curator's job in a museum), geneticist, protozoologist, vertebrate behaviorist, ecologist, pharmacologist, physiologist—several specialists, including cellular physiologist, neurophysiologist, environmental physiologist—microbiologist, biochemist, biophysicist, immunologist, toxicologist, virologist, a biological science writer, an editor, a science administrator with a degree in biology, a director of research, a dean of a science school . . . and so on.

PROFESSIONAL ASSOCIATIONS

SCIENTIFIC SOCIETIES TAKE an interest in helping employers and prospective employees get together. The American Institute of Biological Sciences (AIBS) and the Federation of Societies for Experimental Biology (FASEB) are especially active on behalf of biologists. Each of them operates a placement service. Both candidates and employers register with the service. Lists of candidates are made available to employers three times a year, while lists of positions available are placed in the hands of registered candidates twice each year. At the annual meetings of the AIBS and the FASEB, the placement services arrange for personal interviews. Each year, several hundred biologists get to meet prospective employers in this way. The positions listed are in schools, colleges, government institutions, industrial laboratories, research foundations, or any place where there is a market for biological talent. If you would like further information, either placement service would be glad to answer your questions; the addresses: AIBS, 3900 Wisconsin Ave., N.W., Washington, D.C. 20016; FASEB, 9650 Rockville Pike, Bethesda, Maryland 20014.

PERSONAL CONTACT

AS YOU CAN see, there are several different ways a biologist can use to look for a job. But the most important one, we haven't even mentioned yet; namely, personal contact. In the early stages of his career, just as the young biologist is about ready to graduate from college, he will find that his professor has received notices of fellowships, graduate assistantships, and various teaching and research jobs available for young graduates. At a later stage in his career, our candidate will be just ready to receive his Ph.D., and now his graduate professor and sponsor has a similar list of possibilities. The chances are that in each case the professor is personally acquainted with the prospective employer. In that case, it is more than likely that the personal recommendation of the professor will carry more weight with the employer than any other single document or record the candidate can produce.

The department head who has a vacancy on his staff for a young person will not only write to the schools which operate training programs, but when he goes to a meeting of scientists he will inquire of all his friends: "Do you know a good man or woman I can get to fill this position?" At the larger scientific meetings, the corridors are filled with people on the alert for job opportunities and with others seeking applicants. If you are one of those looking for a job—or if you already have one but think there might be something better—you will find that as your experience and reputation grow you will be more and more likely to be one of those sought out by employers. Biologists are not a restless lot, but there is a considerable amount of ebb and flow of people among jobs. After you become known to other biologists as someone whose work merits attention, you will probably be given chances at more jobs than you can ever fill. The attention paid to you by prospective employers not only gives a lift to your ego, but in many cases opens the eyes of your present boss to your true worth so that you are rewarded with a raise and a promotion to keep you from moving. Then you might join that large group of scientists who like their location so much that they spend virtually their entire working lives on one campus or in one laboratory.

TANGIBLE REWARDS OF A BIOLOGICAL CAREER

AN IDEAL CAREER should be able to provide you with (a) sufficient income to provide you and your family with a standard of living comparable with others of similar education and experience, (b) reasonable opportunity for advancement, (c) recognition by society as one who is engaged in useful work, and (d) a feeling of self-esteem and deep personal satisfaction that comes from work sufficiently challenging to develop one's capabilities to the fullest.

To find out how bioscience measures up in these areas, you might talk with as many biologists as possible. It is a safe prediction that most of them would feel that biology offers a great deal in each category. There may be ways to obtain greater riches, or easier routes to fame (for example, in sports, entertainment, or politics) but most biologists "if they had it all to do over again" would probably choose either the same career or one very much like it.

No exact figures can be given for what your salary as a biologist will be; many factors affect the figure. In recent years, salaries in government laboratories and in educational institutions have been changing from year to year in an upward direction. Laboratories in industry generally pay slightly more than do government labs, which, in turn, offer more than schools, hospitals, or private research foundations. The gaps are not wide, however, and have become so much narrowed in recent years that industry has had to increase its offers in order to preserve any gap at all. Hence, the type of employer you choose will determine your salary to some extent, but the difference may not be great enough to make the size of the salary the principle deciding factor in choosing a job.

Salaries vary somewhat in different sections of the country, but the differential is not great for those holding a Ph.D. degree. The National Science Foundation published the results of a survey of about 21,000 bioscientists holding doctorates, and found approximately 62% of them to be employed by educational institutions, slightly less than 10% by the federal government, and nearly 9% by industry or business.

In round figures, a beginner who has just received a

Bachelor of Science or Bachelor of Arts degree may receive about $6,000 annually if employed as a teacher or as a research assistant in a hospital, university, or privately endowed institution. In a government laboratory, or in some of the better paying school districts, the starting salary would be on the order of $7,000 to $7,500, while in industry it would be about $8,000. After 5 years of experience, the teacher or research assistant with a baccalaureate degree might expect his salary to increase to $9,000 or $11,000, depending upon the place of employment. In industry, salary increases are usually determined on a merit basis, but in many school systems they are mandatory.

High school teachers with Master's degrees may start in a large city school system such as that in New York with a salary as high as $9,000. With automatic raises, the pay eventually goes to $15,000 and even higher if the teacher becomes head of a department. The holder of the Ph.D. degree in physiology, pharmacology, biochemistry, and similar disciplines, can expect to start his career in school, college, or hospital at about $10,000 to $11,000, in government service at about $13,000, or in industry at $14,000.

The figures above are approximately those prevailing during the 1969-70 season. In some of the poorer or more isolated sections of the country, somewhat lower figures may prevail. A survey* recently summarized revealed a strong tendency for recent beginning Ph.D.'s to receive higher starting salaries than did their predecessors, and to enjoy more rapid increases. The top figure that the holder of the baccalaureate degree can expect at the end of a career after serving many years successfully in industry as a laboratory assistant or technician would be about $16,000. The holder of a Ph.D. in the same laboratory might go as high at $25,000 or more without being burdened with

---

* "Careers of Ph.D.'s in the Biosciences," Joan G. Creager and Lindsey R. Harmon, *BioScience,* October, 1969, vol. 19, p. 910.

administrative responsibilities. If he were an administrator and advanced, let us say, to vice-president of his company, the figure could go much higher. The best-paid professors in large universities holding "name" professorships may also be in the $20,000 to $25,000 range.

Most of the figures above were obtained from a personnel officer of a large laboratory, who added that the law of supply and demand also operates, and some specialities in great demand and short supply might command premium salaries. His own laboratory, for example, would gladly pay $2,000 to $4,000 annually above the usual figures to obtain a Ph.D. with special skills in electron microscopy. As this is being written, almost any of the large drug companies would gladly pay a similar premium to a young man or woman with a Ph.D. degree in pathology who also had a knowledge of veterinary medicine—such an individual would probably have obtained a Ph.D. in pathology in a college of veterinary medicine. These are rare birds, indeed—a personnel officer of one company told me that at a recent meeting he attended, several universities and several government laboratories together with some 18 to 20 industrial concerns were looking for just such a person. He was able to locate only two or three.

The salary discussion above, though dealing with only approximate figures, subject to error, and probably out of date by the time they are printed, should be sufficient to convince you of these four things: (1) salaries paid to biologists are in the middle income brackets and are adequate for a reasonable standard of living; (2) merit is rewarded by advancement and by salary increases; (3) it really pays—in dollars and cents as well as in other ways—to obtain the highest degree possible; (4) the most successful biologists do not make as much money as do the most successful physicians, lawyers, or business men. Therefore one should not enter the profession of biological scientist if his primary purpose is to get rich.

INTANGIBLE REWARDS

ALTHOUGH PRACTICALLY EVERYONE needs and appreciates a good pay check, to the average biologist the deepest and most satisfying things about his career come from things no amount of money can buy. Take the high school or college teacher of bioscience. The thrill of watching young people with keen minds react to the excitement of science cannot be described; it can only be experienced. The delight and wonderment which the young show in living things and the satisfaction which the teacher has in observing comprehension and enthusiasm appear on the faces of students are the rewards of teaching. But this is not all. Some of the students will choose bioscience as a career and extend the teacher's influence to yet another generation—and even those who do not choose a career in biological science may continue an interest in living things and an attitude toward life which will reflect the influence of good teaching.

Research work, administration, or any other kind of service in bioscience has intangible rewards no less than those of teaching. Think of the number of people you know to whom their daily work is "just a job." Also think how much of life people miss, if they do not take pleasure and gratification in their day-to-day occupation! If there are any such people in biology, they are in the wrong profession. One of the most obvious things about life science is the enthusiasm most biologists have for their life's work. Not only is the work itself interesting, but most bioscientists take pretty seriously the idea that their efforts are worthwhile and that they can leave the world a little better than they found it. Perhaps this is one reason biologists are so much inclined to talk shop after hours, and maybe it explains why so many of them continue studying, thinking, and working after retirement.

The subject matter of life science is so large and its diversity is so great that no one person can ever understand it all. The opportunities, therefore, for growth and development know no limit, and no matter how great a person's talents or energy may be, bioscience has challenges sufficient for all. Of one thing you can be sure: if you choose a biological career, you need never find life boring.

APPENDIX

ADDITIONAL SOURCES OF INFORMATION

The American Association for the Advancement of Science, 1515 Massachusetts Ave., N.W., Washington, D.C. 20005, has issued a list of career publications in the sciences entitled, *Careers in Science: A Selected Bibliography for High School Students,* 15c.

The American Institute of Biological Sciences, 3900 Wisconsin Ave., N.W., Washington, D.C. 20016, issues without charge a mimeographed list called, *Careers in the Biological Sciences.* The AIBS maintains an Office of Biological Education which will gladly answer questions; many of the brochures listed below can also be obtained from the OBE.

The National Association of Biology Teachers, 1420 N St., Washington, D.C. 20005, published "Careers in Biology Education," a special issue of *The American Biology Teacher,* April, 1968, vol. 30, no. 4. This is a collection of short articles by biology educators both in the classroom and outside it.

The National Vocational Guidance Association, 1605 New Hampshire Avenue, N.W., Washington, D.C. 20009, has prepared a bibliography of current occupational literature, listing brochures and career planning material, originally published in 1963 for $1.00. Additions are published four times a year as *Vocational Guidance Quarterly*—annual subscription, $3.00

BOOKS

Bernard, Jessie. *Academic Women.* Pennsylvania State University Press, 1964. This title is of interest to women considering a career in science.

Fox, W. T. *Careers in the Biological Sciences.* New York: H. Z. Walck, Inc., 1963. A popularly written account of some examples of what has been accomplished by applied research in biology.

Herbert, F. W. *Careers in Natural Resource Conservation.* New York: H. Z. Walck, Inc., 1963. As the title implies, this book covers only one branch of applied biology.

M.I.T. Symposium on American Women in Science and Engineering. M.I.T. Press, 1965. A book of interest to women considering a career in science.

Pollack, P. *Careers and Opportunities in Science.* Revised by J. Purcell. New York: E. P. Dutton & Co., 1968. This title is mostly concerned with the physical sciences, but contains some short chapters on biology and its applications; strongly oriented toward research, with little attention to teaching or other possible careers.

Sarnoff, P. *Careers in Biological Science.* New York: Julian Messner, 1968. The aim of this title is similar to that of the present book, but the point of view is dissimilar, as the author's career has been in economics and finance rather than in bioscience; not all biological disciplines are covered.

Stevens, R. B. *Career Opportunities in Biology.* Publication No. 552 of the National Academy of Sciences - National Research Council, 1957; though out of print, this book is still found in some libraries; can be purchased from University Microfilms Library Services, Ann Arbor, Mich. 48106.

U. S. Department of Agriculture. *Profiles—Careers in the U. S. Department of Agriculture.* Superintendent of Documents, Government Printing Office, Washington, D.C. 20402, $2.00; a comprehensive description of the programs and careers in the U.S.D.A.

Vocational Guidance Manuals (of which the present volume is one). Books in this series containing information related to some of the topics in this book include the volumes on forestry, pharmacy, teaching, and veterinary medicine.

Wachs, T., Jr. *Careers in Research Science.* New York: H. Z. Walck, Inc., 1963. As the title indicates, this is a general discussion of scientific research as a career.

BROCHURES AND ARTICLES

General

Bardach, John E. "Aquaculture," *Science,* vol. 161 (Sept. 13, 1968), p. 1098.

Careers in Biology. American Institute of Biological Sciences, 3900 Wisconsin Ave., N.W., Washington, D.C. 20016.

Careers in Ecology. Dr. S. I. Auerbach, Secretary, Ecological Society of America, Oak Ridge National Laboratory, Radiation Ecology Section, Oak Ridge, Tenn. 37830.

A Career in Genetics. American Genetic Association, 1028 Connecticut Ave., N.W., Washington, D.C. 20036.

"No Room for Negroes in Science?" an interview with Dr. John T. Wilson, *Scientific Research* (May 13, 1968), p. 26.

Rossi, Alice S. "Women in Science: Why so Few?" *Science,* vol. 148 (May 28, 1965), p. 1196.

A Wildlife Conservation Career for You. The Wildlife Society, Suite S176, 3900 Wisconsin Ave., N.W., Washington, D.C. 20016.

Plant Science

Botany as a Profession. Secretary, Botanical Society of America, Department of Botany, Indiana University, Bloomington, Indiana 47401.

Career Guide in Plant Physiology. American Society of Plant Physiologists, P.O. Box 5706, Washington, D.C. 20014.

A Career in Mycology. The Mycological Society of America, New York Botanical Garden, Bronx, New York 10458.

Career Opportunities in the Nursery Industry. American Association of Nurserymen, 835 Southern Building, Washington, D.C. 20005.

Careers in Plant Pathology. The American Phytopathological Society; brochure can be obtained from American Institute of Biological Sciences (address above) or from department of botany or plant pathology in any land grant college.

Horticulture—A Challenging Career. The American Association for Horticultural Science, 615 Elm Street, St. Joseph, Michigan 49085.

Seed Technology Seed Analysis and You. Association of Official Seed Analysists, National Seed Storage Laboratories, Fort Collins, Colorado 80521.

Animal Sciences

Career Opportunities for the Herpetologist and *Career Opportunities for the Ichthyologist.* Dr. Ronal I. Crombie, Secretary, American Society of Ichthyologists and Herpetologists, Division of Reptiles, U. S. National Museum, Washington, D.C. 20560.

Careers in Animal Biology. American Society of Zoologists. brochure can be obtained from AIBS (address above) or from Samuel N. Turiel and Associates, Inc., 333 North Michigan Ave., Chicago, Ill.

Careers in Fisheries Biology. American Fisheries Society, 1404 New York Ave., N.W., Washington, D.C. 20005.

Entomology . . . An Exciting Scientific Career. The Entomological Society of America, 4603 Calvert Road, College Park, Maryland 20740.

Microbiology

Microbiology in Your Future. American Society for Microbiology, 1913
   I St., N.W., Washington, D.C. 20006.
Waksman, Selman A. "Microbiology as a Field of Science and Applica-
   tion," *American Scientist*, vol. 57 (Autumn, 1969), p. 364.

Biomedical Sciences

Biophysics an Exciting New Frontier in Science. The Biophysical Society, P.O. Box 3054, University Station, Columbus, Ohio.

The following societies have offices in the same building, and share
the same address: 9650 Rockville Pike, Bethesda, Maryland 20014; the
brochures listed can be obtained by addressing the Secretary of the society concerned at this address.

The American Physiological Society issues the career brochure *Consider Physiology,* and smaller brochures *Marine Physiology*
                                        Medical Physiology
                                        Comparative Physiology
                                        Veterinary Physiology
                                        Choosing a Career.

The American Society for Pharmacology and Experimental Therapeutics:
   A Career in Pharmacology.

The American Institute of Nutrition:
   Careers in Nutrition.

The American Society of Biological Chemists:
   Careers in Biochemistry.

Intersociety Committee for Research Potential in Pathology:
   A Career in Medical Science—Pathology

   Should you be a Pathologist?, by Alan R.Moritz, M.D.—also
      available from New York Life Insurance Co., Box 51, Madison
      Square Garden Station, New York, N. Y. 10010.

   A Career for you as a Certified Laboratory Assistant—also avail-
      able from Secretary, Board of Certified Laboratory Assistants,
      445 North Lake Shore Drive, Chicago, Illinois 60611.

   *Medical Technology: What Kind of Career Could I have in a
      Medical Laboratory?*—also available from Registry of Medical
      Technologists, 445 North Lake Shore Drive, Chicago, Illinois
      60611.

Government Service

> *The Scientist in the Federal Service,* by John W. Macy, Jr., in *Science,* 2 April, 1965, vol. 148, p. 51.
>
> *Threads of Life,* a career booklet on agricultural science, by the Committee on Educational Policy in Agriculture, Agricultural Board, National Academy of Sciences—National Research Council, 2101 Constitution Ave., Washington, D.C. 20418.

The following booklets prepared by the U.S. Department of Agriculture are obtainable from the U.S.D.A. Office of Information, Washington, D.C. 20250:

> *Scientific Careers in Crops Research* #M.P.-903
>
> *Scientific Careers in the Agricultural Research Service* #M.P.-798
>
> *Careers in Forestry* #M.P.-249
>
> *Careers in Soil Conservation Service* #M.P.-717.

GLOSSARY OF TERMS USED IN THIS BOOK

AGRICULTURAL SCIENCE: Any of several applied biological sciences seeking to discover knowledge about plants and animals and apply the discoveries to the needs of mankind for food or fiber.

AGRONOMY: An applied plant science, usually restricted to crops, often including both the botanical and the soil aspects of crop growth.

AIBS: Initials of the American Institute of Biological Sciences.

ALGOLOGY: A branch of systematic botany dealing with the Algae, simple green plants comprising the seaweeds and similar forms of fresh water and damp places.

ANATOMY: The biological science dealing with the structure of a plant or an animal; used more or less interchangeably with the word *morphology*.

AQUACULTURE: The practical application of biological knowledge to the cultivation of the growth of organisms, usually fish, oysters, or shrimp, in water; analagous to agriculture on land; if sea water is involved, it is often called *mariculture*.

AQUATIC BIOLOGY: Biological science, either basic or applied, concerned with biological events or organisms in water; if sea water is involved, it is usually called *marine biology* and may be considered to be a branch of *oceanography;* as sometimes used, the term *aquatic biology* refers to fresh water and is a branch of *limnology*.

BACTERIOLOGY: The scientific study of the bacteria; a branch of *microbiology*.

BIOCHEMISTRY: The scientific study of the chemistry of living things; the study of living matter or of substances derived from living matter whether plant, animal, or microorganism, by the use of the methods of chemistry.

BIOLOGY: A broad and all-inclusive term for any scientific study of life; all the sciences discussed in this book are branches of biology.

BIOPHYSICS: A branch of biology which uses the tools and concepts of physics to study living matter.

BIOSYSTEMATICS: The branch of biology dealing with the description, classification, and naming of plants and animals (see *taxonomy*), together with whatever features distinguish one species from another, whether anatomical, biochemical, ecological, or what not and any information enabling the bioscientist to place an organism in its place in the evolutionary process; also called *systematics* or *systematic biology*.

BOTANY: The scientific study of plants; a general term including many biological disciplines, as applied to plants.

BRYOLOGY: A branch of systematic botany concerned with mosses and liverworts.

CUEBS: Initials of the Commission on Undergraduate Education in the Biological Sciences.

CYTOLOGY: The scientific study of cells, including structure, formation, biochemistry, and functions.

DENDROLOGY: The branch of botany concerned with trees and shrubs.

ECOLOGY: The scientific sudy of the relationship of an organism—plant, animal, or human—to its environment; sometimes called *bionomics*.

EMBRYOLOGY: The study of organisms in their earliest stages of development; in zoology, before hatching (oviparous animals) or in rudimentary beginning stages (viviparous animals); in botany, the rudimentary plant contained in the seed.

ENDOCRINOLOGY: That branch of physiology concerned with the endocrine glands or other structures which release substances exerting physiological effects at a site other than its point of origin.

ENTOMOLOGY: The scientific study of insects.

FASEB: Initials of the Federation of Societies for Experimental Biology.

FORESTRY: The branch of applied science concerned with all aspects of the planting and care of forest trees.

GENETICS: The science of heredity; concerned with all aspects of the biological processes involved in inheritance, or the passing on of characteristics from one generation to the next.

HEMATOLOGY: The study of blood, including both cellular and fluid parts; also spelled *haematology* (chiefly British).

HERPETOLOGY: A branch of systematic zoology dealing with reptiles and amphibians.

HISTOLOGY: A study of the microscopic structure of the tissues of plant or animal.

HORTICULTURE: A study of the cultivation of garden plants.

ICHTHYOLOGY: A branch of systematic zoology dealing with fishes.

IMMUNOLOGY: The scientific study of the bodily processes involved in immunity to disease, and similar biochemical reactions.

LIMNOLOGY: The scientific study of bodies of fresh water; includes physical, geographic, and other aspects as well as biological; the corresponding study of the ocean is *oceanography*.

MAMMOLOGY: The branch of zoology dealing with mammals, animals that suckle their young.

MARICULTURE: See *aquaculture*.

MARINE BIOLOGY: See *aquatic biology*.

MICROBIOLOGY: The scientific study of microscopic organisms.

MORPHOLOGY: The study of the structure of an organism without regard to function; same as *anatomy*.

MYCOLOGY: A branch of systematic botany dealing with fungi; that is, yeasts, molds, and mushrooms.

NABT: Initials of the National Association of Biology Teachers.

NSMRSE: Initials of the National Study of Mathematics Requirements for Scientists and Engineers.

OBE: Initials of the Office of Biological Education, an agency of AIBS.

OCEANOGRAPHY: The scientific study of the oceans.

ORGANISM: Any living form, whether an animal, a plant, a bacterium, or other.

ORNITHOLOGY: A branch of systematic zoology dealing with birds.

PARASITOLOGY: The scientific study of parasites; that is, of plants or animals which obtain their nutriment by living in or upon other living bodies.

PATHOLOGY: The scientific study of disease, including its origin, nature, and effects upon the body.

PHARMACOLOGY: The scientific study of the effects of foreign chemical substances upon bodily functions; the study of drugs and their effects on the body.

PHYSIOLOGY: The scientific study of functions of living organisms or of any of their parts.

PHYTOPATHOLOGY: The study of the diseases of plants.

PLANKTON: Small plants (phytoplankton) or animals (zooplankton) that float or drift about in the water, especially those near the surface; plankton are at the bottom of the food pyramid—they are eaten by larger creatures.

PLANT PATHOLOGY: See *phytopathology*.

PLANT PHYSIOLOGY: The study of functions of plant organisms or of any of their parts.

RICKETTSIA: Bacteria-like organisms living as parasites in ticks, etc., causing certain diseases, such as Rocky Mountain spotted fever; Rickettsiae are microorganisms differing in certain details from bacteria or viruses.

SYSTEMATICS; SYSTEMATIC BIOLOGY: See *biosystematics*.

TAXONOMY: Description, classification, and naming of organisms, an integral part of biosystematics.

TECHNICIAN: In the biology laboratory, a technician is a laboratory worker who is skilled in the art and technique of biology and is a valuable assistant to the professional scientist in charge of the laboratory, and who may supervise other technicians, but who lacks the theoretical background or experience to have full charge of complex operations such as research projects.

TECHNOLOGIST: A technician; as commonly used, a technologist may have a higher degree of formal training than a technician (as these terms are officially employed by the American Society of Clinical Pathologists, for example).

VIROLOGY: The study of viruses and of the diseases caused by them.

VIRUS: An infectious agent requiring living cells for propagation; viruses are smaller than bacteria.

ZOOLOGY: The scientific study of animals; a general term including many biological disciplines as applied to animals.

INDEX